D1217127

CIVIL ENGINEERING 1839–1889

A PHOTOGRAPHIC HISTORY

PLATE 1 G.W. Keeling inside the cylinders for the bridge piers for the Severn Railway Bridge, 8 May 1877. 9.25 in. x 7 in. Engineer: T.E. Harrison; contractor: Windsor Iron Works, Liverpool

'Nearly all the photographs were taken by myself and often when light was unsuitable, so I trust every allowance will be made for defects due to amateur and unskillful treatment and bad light.

'The photographs are only details of the structure and of the means employed to erect the bridge – and may therefore be of interest to some members of the Institution' – G.W. Keeling

CIVIL ENGINEERING 1839–1889

A PHOTOGRAPHIC HISTORY

MIKE CHRIMES

FOREWORD BY PROFESSOR ROY SEVERN
President of the Institution of Civil Engineers

To
Elsie, Joe, Ted and Maud
who gave me the opportunities
they never had

A Budding Book

First published in the United Kingdom in 1991
by Alan Sutton Publishing Limited, an imprint of Sutton Publishing Limited.

This edition published in 1997 by Budding Books, an imprint of
Sutton Publishing Limited · Phoenix Mill · Thrupp · Stroud · Gloucestershire

British Library Cataloguing in Publication Data

Chrimes, Mike
Civil engineering 1839–89 : a photographic history.
I. Title
624.09

ISBN 1-84015-008-4

Typeset in 10/12pt Times.
Typesetting and origination by
Sutton Publishing Limited.
Printed in Great Britain by
WBC Limited, Bridgend.

Contents

List of Photographs

Foreword

Mike Chrimes is well known to members of the Institution of Civil Engineers as its highly esteemed Librarian, whose interest in, and knowledge of, all aspects of construction is freely placed at their disposal. His grasp of the history of our profession is second to none, and in this book he has culled some of the vast treasure which our library contains to present a pictorial history of civil engineering during the fifty-year period 1839-1889, an era which saw the end of the major canal period, the beginnings of the railway boom, with the completion of the Forth Bridge in 1890, and the start of construction of the Manchester Ship Canal.

The period which he has chosen is often referred to, with justification, as the 'golden period' of civil engineering, seeing great strides, not only in modes of transportation, but also in the public health field, with much attention to the supply of clean water and efficient sewerage disposal. Thus, whereas the popular image is satisfied by giants such as Brunel and the Stephensons, the greatest social good to the greatest number was provided by Bazalgette, the creator of London's sewerage disposal system.

His deep study in the re-organization and cataloguing of the Institution's archival material has given Mike Chrimes the opportunity to piece together a fascinating book, which places not only civil engineers but anyone interested in the development of civilized society greatly in his debt. Much of the physical infrastructure which he refers to is now in the process of necessary change to fit different requirements, making this photographic record of very significant value.

R.T. Severn
President
The Institution of Civil Engineers

Acknowledgements

My acknowledgements are many for this work, and I can only name a few: Paul Parkes for typing my many drafts; David Buri, a former colleague, who gave me the time to organize the exhibition at the Institution of Civil Engineers to celebrate 150 years of photography from which this book stems, and who copied many of the photographs; Corin Hughes-Stanton (Features Editor, *New Civil Engineer*) who, I am sure, shares my belief in the importance of civil engineering photography as an art form; Chris Baker and Grant Smith, past and present photographers at *New Civil Engineer*; John Ward of the Science Museum, for helpful advice; and Francis Pugh, whose own exhibition work encouraged me. There are also the many helpful discussions I have had over the years with members of the Institution of Civil Engineers and Institution of Structural Engineers History Group. The biggest debt of all goes to the late John James; without his generous donation, this book and the Institution's archives would be immeasurably poorer.

Unless otherwise stated the photographs are taken from the Institution's collections, and were reprinted by myself, David Buri, Grant Smith or Chris Baker. The author and publishers are also grateful to the following for permission to reproduce photographs: Blyth & Blyth, page 27; Coode Blizzard, pages 74 and 130; Durban Local History Library, pages 156 and 165; Imperial College, Department of Civil Engineering, pages 54 and 125; Library of Congress, page 137; Museum of London in Docklands (Corporation of London), page 77; National Railway Museum, page 40; North West Water, plc, page 90; Roland Paxton, page 50; Powisland Museum, page 48; Public Records Office, page 37; Royal Botanic Gardens, Kew, page 33; Royal Engineers, page 41; Royal Library, Windsor, pages 5 and 7; Royal Photographic Society, page 58; Science Museum, page 160; Smithsonian Institution, pages 137 and 142; Strathclyde Regional Council, page 88. The figures on pages 5 and 7 are reproduced by gracious permission of HM The Queen.

CHAPTER ONE

Introduction

Les images photographiques . . . permetront . . . de remonter aux dimensions exactes des parties les plus elevées, les plus inaccessibles des edifices.

Arago, 1839.[1]

If one image has come to symbolize the entrepreneurial confidence of the Victorian age it is the photograph by Robert Howlett of I.K. Brunel standing in front of the launching drum of the *Great Eastern*. In the popular mind this is the photograph of Victorian engineering. This book sets out to demonstrate that there was much more to nineteenth-century civil engineering.

It is now just over 150 years since the term 'photography' was first used by Sir John Herschel[2,3] to describe the processes developed by Daguerre[4,5] and Fox Talbot[6] to reproduce the images of nature by the use of light-sensitive chemicals. The early history of photography is now well-known, yet the extent and importance of industrial and engineering photography has been largely overlooked.

To obtain some idea of the scale of the contribution of civil engineers to nineteenth-century photography one needs to be aware that members of the profession at that time worked in all disciplines of engineering, not just those parts most closely associated with construction. They included many people with a scientific curiosity and natural inventiveness, just the sort of people to take to the new discovery. In large parts of the globe engineers were responsible for the earliest detailed surveys and exploration of an area, and they recorded their experiences on camera. They were not just concerned with engineering processes, but also with architecture, for which they were often responsible, particularly in the colonies. The importance of photography in achieving an accurate record of engineering work was recognized almost immediately, and by the time Brunel was posing for photographs at the launch of the *Great Eastern* the idea of professional photographers being commissioned to record an engineering project was well established.

The main uses to which photography could be put by engineers were outlined as early as 12 May 1840 by Alexander Gordon at a meeting of the Institution of Civil Engineers. They were 'enabling copies of drawings, or views of buildings, or even of machinery when not in motion, to be taken with perfect accuracy in a very short space of time and with comparatively small expense'.[7] There was nothing particularly perspicacious about Gordon's remarks. They were logical developments when one considers the origins of photography, and bear a striking resemblance to Arago's remarks when advocating that the French state bought the rights to the daguerreotype for the public.[8]

Photographs were frequently used as the basis for illustrations in technical and general interest magazines. There were reproduction problems in early years which civil engineers attempted to solve. The French civil engineer and photographer Poitevin introduced photolithography in 1855, and Walter Bentley Woodbury, who worked on Melbourne Waterworks, developed 'Woodburytypes'.

The fifty years following the invention of photography was not only a period of rapid advance in photography but it also saw rapid industrial advance as the rest of the world caught up with, and in some cases overtook, the industrial achievements of Great Britain. The most spectacular developments were in infrastructure. In 1839 railways were just beginning to have an impact on the British economy and landscape, the great age of municipal improvements was yet to begin, and large areas of the globe remained unexplored by Europeans and totally without modern transport systems.

The early photographs that survive of engineering subjects are by and large topographic views of bridges, among them Daguerre's views of bridges over the Seine[9] and Fox Talbot's photograph of I.K. Brunel's Hungerford Suspension Bridge, *c.* 1845. The earliest photographs to show views of civil engineering construction sites were Fox Talbot's 1843 calotype of the scaffolding at the base of Nelson's Column (see Plate 2),[10] and two daguerreotypes of the Palm House under construction at Kew in 1847 (see Plate 23). It seems likely early photographs of civil engineering projects remain to be discovered, and the recent discovery of three photographs of Britannia Tubular Bridge under construction in 1849[11] supports this.

The best-documented instance of early civil engineering photography is the work of J.C. Bourne and Roger Fenton for Charles Blacker Vignoles at the Kiev Suspension Bridge.[12,13] Vignoles was later to become President of the Institution of Civil Engineers. By 1846 he was a well-established civil engineer, who had a number of scientific interests, including photography and astronomy, outside the engineering profession, reflected in his election to the Royal

PLATE 2 Scaffolding at the foot of Nelson's Column. This copy of a calotype is possibly the earliest surviving photograph of a civil engineering construction site. The scaffolding at the base of the column was developed specially by the contractor Grissell for the erection of the column.
Contractor: T. Grissell; photographer: W.H. Fox Talbot, 1843

Society. When Vignoles was successful in getting his design for a suspension bridge across the Dnieper at Kiev accepted by the Tsar he seems to have been determined that a photographic record be made of the erection of the bridge. By this time the idea of publishing detailed, lavishly-illustrated accounts of civil engineering projects was well established. John Cook Bourne had demonstrated his ability with his illustrations of the work on the London and Birmingham Railway (1839) and Great Western Railway (1846). It is clear from the drawings in the Elton Collection that the London and Birmingham illustrations were based on detailed sketches of the navvies at work.[14] With such attention to accurate detail one can imagine Bourne would have been very interested in photography as an aid to his work as a topographic artist. He accompanied Vignoles to Russia as resident artist, and in 1852 Roger Fenton followed. The result was a

PLATE 3 Kiev Bridge, 1852.
14 in x 11 in, from an original salt print in a private collection.
Engineer: C.B. Vignoles;
contractors: Fox Henderson (chains) and Musgrave & Sons;
photographer: J.C. Bourne

magnificent album of photographs presented to the Tsar. These can have represented only a small proportion of those taken every week between 1847 and 1852,[15] some of which were shown to Queen Victoria.[16]

Vignoles would have an important place in the history of photography even without being possibly the first civil engineer to commission an official photographer, at Kiev. He played an important role in the foundation of the Royal Photographic Society,[17] and was keen that engineers should take advantage of the new technology. While in Russia he attempted to photograph an eclipse, and was later to organize photographs of the total eclipse of the sun on 18 July 1860 while working on the Bilbao–Tudela Railway in Spain.[18,19] The success of the expedition, and Vignoles' role, was reported by De La Rue to the Royal Society in 1862.[20]

Improved photographic techniques coincided with the Great Exhibition in 1851. This provided an ideal opportunity for photographers to demonstrate their skills, and the successful publication of some of their work in presentation sets of the exhibition catalogue.[21,22] Photographs of the demolition prompted Philip Delamotte, Professor of Drawing at King's College, to be commissioned to record the reconstruction of the Crystal Palace in

PLATE 4 Dismantling Crystal Palace after the Great Exhibition. Engineer: Fox Henderson; photographer: P.H. Delamotte, 1852

1852–3.[23] These photographs are often cited as the earliest complete photographic record of the construction of a building.

The impact of the Great Exhibition is difficult to conceive today. It seized the popular imagination, and was difficult for engineers and manufacturers to ignore. Many must have been alerted to the possibilities that photography offered as a means of advertising products or recording construction.

One cannot be absolutely certain of the chronology but more or less contemporaneously James Mudd began to take photographs of the Longdendale Valley reservoirs for the Manchester Waterworks scheme, a series which continued into the 1870s.[24] It is possible that photographs taken of the Crystal Palace exhibits may have encouraged the Manchester engineering firm Beyer–Peacock to employ Mudd to take photographs of their locomotives from *c.* 1854 onwards.[25] Such photographs became increasingly common as the century progressed, with backgrounds being wiped out, so that the locomotive, or other engineering product, became itself a work of art.

By the mid-1850s there was a growing acceptance by the engineering profession and others, of the merit in recording

PLATE 5 South Kensington Museum under construction. Ironwork: C.D. Young & Company; photographer: Captain Milliken (J.G. James Collection)

engineering works. This was recognized by the engineers in Government Service. Although nominally military engineers, the Royal Engineers were responsible for much civil work, and made substantial contributions to the development of photography as well as to the photographic recording of engineering works.

Photography was first used by the military in 1848 in India by John MacCosh, a surgeon working for the forces of the East India Company in Bengal. He took calotypes of the Second Sikh War (1848–9) and the Second Burma War (1852–3).[26]

It is unclear when the Royal Engineers first began to encourage the photography of their civil engineering works. Some sappers assisted Charles Thurston Thompson with the photographic exhibits at the Great Exhibition.[27] Thompson subsequently became official photographer to the Department of Science and Art and their South Kensington museum. The department regarded photography as important in providing 'specimens of the highest objects of art at the cheapest possible rate' for schools of art and the general public in an attempt to improve on the poor quality of design revealed at the Great Exhibition.[28] Some of the Royal Engineers had been stationed at the site of the South Kensington museum to act as firemen and carry out other work. In 1856 it was decided they should be given a course in photography by Thompson. Three of the sappers, Corporals Sparkman, Milliken and Church, were responsible for some of the earliest civil engineering photographs – those of the construction of the iron structure of the South Kensington museum.[29,30] Although much of the early work

PLATE 6 Paris–Boulogne Railway, 1855. 25 in x 18.5 in. Photographer: E. Baldus

by the sappers was associated with the museum, some engineers were sent to Thompson for instruction before being sent overseas to photograph work in progress, and some others were trained in Paris at the 1855 Exhibition and subsequently worked for the Ordnance Survey.[31]

In 1855 Lieutenant Colonel James, RE, head of the Ordnance Survey, carried out experiments using photography to copy maps and in 1860 he introduced a printing process known as photozincography (a variant of photolithography).[32,33] This was to be used to produce replicas of the Domesday Book and other historical manuscripts.[34]

Apart from James, the most distinguished military contributor to the development of photography at the time was Captain W. de W. Abney, RE. He made his reputation in photography in India, and on his return to England set up a course on photography at the newly reconstituted School of Military Engineering in 1871.[35] His textbook for the Royal Engineers provided all the information required for an engineer to set out on a photographic expedition.[36] The result of the encouragement of Abney and his colleagues was

PLATE 7 Gare d'Austerlitz, Paris. 13 in x 9.5 in. The station was rebuilt 1865–7, and this impressive 52 m-span roof was erected, with Polonceau roof trusses, by the leading French ironworks of Schneider & Company at Le Creusot. Engineer: L. Sevene; contractor: Schneider & Company; photographer: E. Baldus

that Royal Engineers took photographs of civil engineering works wherever they were engaged, at home and overseas.

Development in France seems to have been very similar with government engineers involved in photography from the 1850s.[37] The administration of the Ponts et Chaussées commissioned Hippolyte Auguste Collard to take photographs of major bridge projects between 1857 and 1868, and regional engineers followed this example.[38] Private enterprise also made a significant contribution. Baron Rothschild commissioned Edouard Baldus to photograph the Paris–Boulogne Railway line for a presentation album for Queen Victoria when she used the railway to visit the Paris Exhibition in 1855,[39] and Nadar's experiments with underground photography in the Paris catacombs at the end of 1861 attracted the attention of the Paris municipal authorities whose sewerage scheme was near completion. In early 1862 he took about twenty-three photographs of the sewers, some of the few photographs taken of underground civil engineering works in the nineteenth century.[40] In 1864 Charles Garnier employed two photographers, Delmaet and Durandelle, on the construction site of the Paris Opera, one of the earliest instances of a documentary record of a construction site showing men at work.

The high quality of French photographic recording of civil engineering works was brought to the attention of the world at the Vienna Exhibition of 1873. Twenty-two albums of photographs by Baldus and his contemporaries were exhibited by the Ministry of Public Works. Due to the success of the exhibition the best views were published by Rothschild in a series of five albums entitled *Les Travaux Publics de la France*, with the blessing of the Ministry (see Plate 7).

Despite official involvement in record photography of this period, it is the work of the entrepreneur which has captured the imagination of the public, above all the photogrpahs of the *Great Eastern*. Although Brunel's is the name associated with the project, it seems that John Scott Russell, the engineer responsible for the construction of the ship, commissioned the first photographs. Between 1854 and 1856 Joseph Cundall took progress photographs for Russell twice a month, copies of which were forwarded to Brunel. A more famous series were taken by Robert Howlett of the launch of the *Great Eastern*, including the famous image of I.K. Brunel in front of the chains. They were sold as stereocards and cartes-de-visite, credited to both Howlett and George Downes.[41]

PLATE 8 John Scott Russell, naval architect, builder of the SS *Great Eastern*. Cabinet photograph, 5.75 in x 3.75 in, by Maull & Fox. Cabinets replaced cartes-de-visite in commercial portrait photography, following their introduction by F.R. Windsor in 1866

Brunel continued to use photographers and Roger Fenton was employed in 1857–8 to photograph the Royal Albert Bridge, Saltash, under construction. One of his views was the earliest photograph to be reproduced in a civil engineering textbook.[42]

Brunel was not a pioneer in his use of photography. The distinguished water engineer, John Bateman, for example, had extensive record photographs taken of the Manchester and Glasgow waterworks schemes in the 1850s and '60s.[43] These are virtually unknown today. However, the commercial success of the photographs of Brunel's works must have meant professional photographers would look favourably on further commissions, to record engineers' works either as a construction record, or with a view to publicity, or both.

The growth of photography in the 1850s was a worldwide phenomenon and from 1860 there are grounds to believe that most major civil engineering projects were recorded on camera, either by professionals or amateurs. In India this period coincided with the introduction of railways. The earliest photographs sent to the Institution of Civil Engineers were those of the construction of the Thul Ghat incline on the Great Indian Peninsula Railway.[44] Unfortunately, these no longer survive. It is evident that photographs were taken of the construction of all the main railways in India on the initiative of civil engineers.[45,46] The same was true for hydraulic works.[47,48] The extent to which official policy affected

PLATE 9 I.K. Brunel in front of the checking drum of the *Great Eastern*. 10.25 in x 9 in. Photographer: R. Howlett, 1857

this is uncertain, but in 1855 the head of the college for East India Company cadets at Addiscombe decided students should be given some instruction in photography,[49] and the following year Dr Hunter advocated photographic training in the Public Works Department at Madras.[50] In 1858 the Army in India was issued with photographic equipment.[51] Whether by official design or amateur enthusiasm the tremendous achievements of British engineers in India in the second half of the nineteenth century were captured on camera.

Elsewhere in the world a broadly similar pattern of development can be seen, the extent of government involvement varying from country to country. In the United States of America, in the early years of photography, daguerreotypes held sway. Among the more unusual subjects thus photographed were Wright's daguerreotype of a train wreck in Rhode Island in 1853, possibly the first photograph of a railway accident.[52] The earliest example of extensive use of photography to record civil engineering projects seems to have been due to Montgomery Cunningham Meigs, who was the military engineer responsible for the construction of Washington's Capitol and post office buildings and its Potomac water-supply scheme in the 1850s.[53]

Apart from Meigs' work prior to *c.* 1867 the majority of views of civil engineering structures appear to have been the work of commercial studios. Of particular interest is the way in which engineering firms began in the late 1850s to use professional photographers to record and publicize their products.[54] Photographs were sent to journals to illustrate articles or for advertisements. Prospective customers were sent photographs.

The American Civil War opened new horizons for photography in the States. Led by Matthew Brady, a group of photographers made their name, and when at the end of the war they sought new epics to record, government and railway surveys were the obvious subjects. In this process the railway companies themselves took an interest, and it is arguable that the photographs of the transcontinental railways taken in the 1860s are the finest examples of railway photography, set against the epic landscape of a largely unknown continent.[55,56]

In Australia, by the time the railways were being built in the mid-1850s photography was well-established. In Sydney in 1857 there were thirty amateur and twenty-five professional photographers.[57]

In the United Kingdom, surviving archives from the 1870s in the files of consultants like Blyth & Blyth and Coode Blizzard indicate it was becoming common to keep some sort of photographic record of progress on a contract. From the somewhat self-effacing letters which accompanied the contractors' albums of the time it is clear such a practice was not yet universal. By the 1880s numbers of surviving photographs indicate it had become commonplace. By then a large number of photographs of civil engineering works had been taken, some commissioned by railway or dock companies, some by public works departments or utilities, some by contractors or consultants, others by manufacturers.

PLATE 10 Joining of the rails, Transcontinental Railroad, Promontory Point, Utah, 10 May 1867. Photographer: A.J. Jackson (J.G. James Collection)

The achievements of civil engineering photography now came together to record lasting achievements of the structural engineers of the time: the Eiffel Tower in France, and the Forth Railway Bridge in Britain. While the engineering achievement of the Eiffel Tower tends to be trivialized by its role as a tourist attraction, its erection provided an ideal subject for the photographer interested in making a dramatic visual record of construction progress, while the very size and scale of the Forth Railway Bridge made it possible for individual structural elements to become suitable subjects for the photographer. A magnificent set of progress photographs was taken between 1883 and 1890 by Evelyn Carey, a civil engineer working on the bridge for Fowler and Baker, the consultants – possibly the most complete photographic record of the construction of any nineteenth-century structure.[58] Photographs were also taken by the contractors, notably by Joseph Phillips' son Peter.

At the first meeting of the Royal Photographic Society Vignoles had spoken of the 'great services which the new art would be likely to render to engineers and others having to superintend important works they could only occasionally visit, or having to make

PLATE 11 Forth Railway Bridge, view of pier and base of main tower under construction from one of Benjamin Baker's slides

intelligible to foreign employers . . . the details of . . . complicated constructions'.[59] Engineers took advantage of the new medium for these and other reasons. For the engineer photography meant that he would have a record of the work carried out, in case of future contractual conflicts or structural problems, at a relatively low cost; photographs once taken could be used to promote the consultant, contractor or manufacturer in attracting future clients; photography could be used to monitor structures and illustrate weaknesses; and photography could be used to record the results of experiments and tests far more accurately than before.

Some of the photographs, taken in photography's first fifty years, are high quality, and testify to the role of civil engineers in advancing this new art form; others are less noteworthy, and bear witness to the amateur hand that guided them, or the difficult conditions under which they were produced. This selection is designed to stimulate further interest and provide an important record of the way in which civil engineering changed the way people lived all over the world.

NOTES

1. Arago, F., 'Le Daguerreotype', Academie des Sciences, *Comptes rendus*, vol. 9, 1839, pp. 250–67.
2. Herschel, Sir J.F.W., 'Note of the art of photography, or the application of the chemical rays of light to the purposes of pictorial representation', *Philosophical Magazine*, vol. 14, 1839, pp. 365–7.
3. Herschel, Sir J.F.W., 'On the chemical action of the rays of the solar spectrum on preparations of silver and other substances, both metallic and non-metallic, and on some photographier processes', Royal Society, *Philosophical Transaction*, 1840, pp. 1–59.
4. Arago, F., 'Fixation des images qui se forment au foyer d'une chambre obscura', Academie des Sciences, *Comptes rendus*, vol. 8, 1839, pp. 4–7.
5. Arago, F., 'Le Daguerreotype', Academie des Sciences, *Comptes rendus*, vol. 9, 1839, pp. 250–67.
6. Talbot, W.H.F., 'Some account of the art of photogenic drawing', *Philosophical Magazine*, vol. 14, 1839, pp. 196–208.
7. Gordon, A., 'Photography as applicable to engineering', ICE *Minutes of Proceedings*, vol. 1, 1840, pp. 57–9.
8. Arago, F., op. cit. (1839), p. 259.
9. Arago, F., 'Fixation des images qui se forment au foyer d'une chambre obscura', Academie des Sciences, *Comptes rendus*, vol. 8, 1839, p. 5.
10. The scaffolding is described in: Grissell, T., 'Account of the scaffolding used in erecting the "Nelson Column", Trafalgar Square', ICE *Minutes of Proceedings*, vol. 3, 1844, pp. 203–17.
11. Hughes Stanton, Corin, 'Who shot Britannia Bridge?', *New Civil Engineer*, 20 August 1978, pp. 40–2. Latimer Clark (brother of Edwin), who worked on the bridge himself, was well known for his interest in photography, but does not appear to have been responsible.
12. Vignoles, O.J., *Life of Charles Blacker Vignoles, FRS FRAS MRIA, etc.*, London: Longmans, 1889, especially pp. 390–2.
13. Vignoles, K.H., *Charles Blacker Vignoles: the romantic engineer*, Cambridge: University Press, 1982.
14. Smithson, A. & P., *Euston Arch*, London: Thames & Hudson, 1968, pp. 2–3, 37, 64–5.
15. Vignoles, C.B., Photographic Society, *Journal*, vol. 1, 1853, p. 5.
16. Vignoles, O.J., op. cit., p. 391, Footnote 1.
17. Vignoles, O.J., *Life of Charles Blacker Vignoles, FRS FRAS MRIA, etc.*, London: Longmans, 1889, especially pp. 390–2.
18. Vignoles, O.J., op. cit., pp. 378–84.
19. 'The total eclipse of the sun', Photographic Society, *Journal*, vol. 6, 1860, pp. 271–3.
20. De la Rue, Warren, 'The Bakerian lecture: on the total solar eclipse of July 18, 1860 observed at Rivabellosa, near Miranda de Ebro in Spain', Royal Society, *Philosophical Transactions*, 1862, pp. 333–416.
21. *Exhibition of the works of industry of all nations, 1851. Reports by the Juries on the subjects in the 30 classes into which the exhibition was divided*, London: Spicer Brothers, 1852.
22. Keeler, N.B., 'Illustrating the Report by the Juries of the Great Exhibition of 1851 . . .', *History of Photography*, vol. 6, 1982, pp. 257–72.
23. Delamotte, P.H., *Photographic views of the progress of the Crystal Palace, Sydenham. Taken during the progress of the works*, London: Photographic Institution, 1855.
24. Quayle, T., *Reservoirs in the hills*, Glossop: North West Water, 1990, pp. 12, 14, 47.
25. Photographers' Gallery, *British industrial photography 1843–1986*, London: The Gallery, 1986, pp. 12–13.
26. Clammer, D., *The Victorian army in photographs*, Newton Abbot: David & Charles, 1975, p. 9.
27. Physick, J., *Photography and the South Kensington Museum*, London: HMSO, 1975, p. 3.
28. Cole, H., *Evidence to: Select Committee on the South Kensington Museum, 1860*.

29. Physick, J., *Photography and the South Kensington Museum*, 1975, passim.
30. Stamp, G., *The Changing Metropolis*. Harmondsworth: Viking, 1984, plate 176.
31. Physick, J., *Photography and the South Kensington Museum*, 1975, pp. 3–4.
32. Reduction of plans by photography in: *Report of the progress of the Ordnance Survey and Topographic Department to 31 December 1859*, pp. 5–6.
33. James, Colonel Sir Henry, 'The practical details of photo-zincography . . .', Royal Engineers, *Papers, New Series*, vol. 10, 1861, pp. 129–32.
34. Photozincography and photography: *Report of the progress of the Ordnance Survey to the 31 December 1874:* [c. 1204].
35. Porter, W., *History of the Corps of Royal Engineers*, vol. 2, 1889, pp. 187–8.
36. Abney, Lieutenant W. de W., *Instruction in photography for use at the SME Chatham,* Chatham: SME, 1871.
37. Lemagny, J-C., and Rouille, A., *A history of photography,* Cambridge: University Press, 1987, pp. 46–7, 55–6.
38. The École des Ponts et Chaussées commenced its first photographic course in 1858. Information from M. Yvon, ENPC.
39. Dimond, F. and Taylor, R., *Crown and camera,* London: Penguin, 1987, p. 122.
40. Howes, C., *To Photograph Darkness*, Gloucester: Alan Sutton, 1989, pp. 1–17.
41. Powell, R., *Photography and the making of history: Brunel's Kingdom*, Bristol: Watershed Media Centre, 1985, pp. 19–30; 48–56.
42. Humber, W., *A complete treatise on cast and wrought iron bridges,* London: Lockwood, 1861.
43. Quayle, T., op. cit., Albums in possession of Strathclyde Regional Council and North West Water.
44. The photographs were presented on behalf of G. Wythes, the contractor for the works, ICE *Minutes of Proceedings*, vol. 26, p. 163, Annual Report of ICE for 1866–7.
45. Engraving of Singaram Viaduct, East India Railway, from a photograph by S.E. Stewart, *Engineers Journal* (Calcutta), vol. 1, 1858, p. 183; Bhallee Khal Viaduct, vol. 2, 1859, p. 6; Satgaon Viaduct, vol. 2, pp. 138–9.
46. Nerbudda Viaduct, from a photograph by A. Jacob, CE, *Engineers Journal*, vol. 2, 1859, pp. 185–6.
47. Glover, T.G., *The Ganges Canal: illustrated by photographs,* Roorkee: Thomason Engineering College Press, 1864, reprinted 1867.
48. Solani Aqueduct (Ganges Canal), photograph by James Freeman, *Professional Papers on Indian Engineering*, vol. 1, 1863–4, Frontispiece.
49. India Office Records L/MIL/1/70, 18 April 1855. Cited in: Thomas, G., 'The first four decades of photography in India', *History of Photography,* vol. 3, 1979, p. 219.
50. Thomas, G., (1979) op. cit., pp. 217–18.
51. Thomas, G., (1979) op. cit., p. 219. Other examples were scrapbooks kept by engineers such as Henry Winship. Sotheby's sale catalogue, 1–5–87, item 34. See also Chapter Eleven.
52. Newhall, B., *The Daguerreotype in North America*, third edition, New York: Dover, 1976, Plate 26.
53. Information from William Worthington, Smithsonian Institution, 22 January, 12 February 1990.
54. White, J.H. jr, 'The steam engine in prints and photographs', *Railroad history*, 152, 1985, pp. 29–41.
55. Schodek, D.L., *Landmarks in American civil engineering,* Cambridge, Mass: MIT, 1987, pp. 52–3.
56. Williamson, G.G., 'Alfred Hart: photographer of the Central Pacific Railroad', *History of photography,* vol. 12, 1, 1988, pp. 61–75.
57. Haes, F., 'On photography in Australia', Photographic Society, *Journal*, vol. 5, 1857–8, p. 179.
58. Carey, E.G., 'Photography in compressed air', *Industries*, 20 April 1888, p. 400.
59. Vignoles, C.B., Photographic Society, *Journal*, vol. 1, 1853, p. 5.

CHAPTER TWO

The Origins and Practice of Civil Engineering

Engineers, civil, a denomination which comprises an order or profession of persons highly respectable for their talents and scientific attainments, and currently useful under this application, as the canals, docks, harbours, lighthouses, etc., employ and honourably testify. This order of artists is said to have commenced in this country about the year 1760, at which period the advancement of the arts and sciences was singularly rapid . . .

Rees Cyclopaedia, c. *1819.*

Although the history of civil engineering is as old as civilization itself, and some of the most spectacular achievements of civil engineers are associated with the ancient world – the pyramids of Egypt, Roman aqueducts, and Mesopotamian irrigation networks are all universally famous, probably more so than their modern equivalents – the development of civil engineering as a distinct profession in the British Isles is normally dated to the second half of the eighteenth century. The growth in trade and associated transport improvements created demand for professional engineers to draw up schemes for investors and provide the expertise necessary to secure the passage of proposals through the legislative process in Parliament, and supervise their construction. For the first time two people – John Smeaton and Thomas Yeoman – are described as civil engineers in a 1763 London directory. In 1768 Smeaton described himself as 'civil engineer' for the first time in a printed report on the Forth Clyde Navigation. This usage reflected a growth in professional self-awareness culminating in the foundation of the Society of Civil Engineers on 15 March 1771 by Smeaton and other leaders of the profession such as Yeoman and Robert Mylne.

This period is often known as the canal age, but canals formed only one part of the work of the engineers of the time, and such a simple linkage tends to obscure the range and scale of civil engineering work of the period. The eighteenth century was also a period of road improvement. From the time the first toll-gate was introduced on the Great North Road at Wadesmill in 1663, a growing number of turnpike trusts required surveyors to introduce and maintain improvements. Work was also available in the port improvements of the time which saw Liverpool and Hull developing their dock systems, and a series of harbour improvements elsewhere reflecting the growth in trade. These developments in particular provided some of the first permanent public authority posts for civil engineers, with dock engineers appointed at Liverpool from 1710 and harbour engineers at Sunderland in the 1720s and at Scarborough from 1731.

These transport developments are only part of the story of civil engineering. The term 'civil engineer' is an attempt to differentiate between the civil and military branches of engineering. While Smeaton originally described himself as 'engineer', engineers had hitherto usually been considered as practitioners of the military art. Many early engineering works were the achievements of military engineers. In the United Kingdom one can point to the constructional achievements of James of St George in the Edwardian castles of North Wales. The Marshal of France, Vauban, is seen as one of the forerunners of the science of soil mechanics. His military experience was important in developing safe rules for the construction of embankments and retaining walls, such important features of canal, railway and dock construction.

By the mid-eighteenth century much engineering work had been done in a non-military context. Millwork and associated wind and water power had been gradually improved and refined since the Middle Ages; the demands of the mining industry played a significant part in the development of tunnelling techniques (to win the minerals), early railways or plateways (to transport them), and, as mines went deeper, in creating a demand for pumps for drainage, powered by steam engines from the late seventeenth century onwards. Land reclamation and drainage works dating from the medieval period can be seen in Kent, Somerset, the Fens and Lincolnshire. In the seventeenth century the Bedford Level was created as part of a commercial venture, with the Dutch engineer Cornelius Vermuyden being imported to draw up the plans. All these works were the achievements of the forerunners of the modern civil engineer.

By the late eighteenth century the technical literature contains sufficiently detailed illustrations to enable a reasonable impression of how bridges were erected, mills constructed and hydraulic works carried out. Some works, such as Belidor's *Architecture*

PLATE 12 Foundation for pier 2, Pont de Neuilly, *c.* 1768. Engineer: J.R. Peronnet

hydraulique and Perronet's *Description des projets et de la construction des ponts de Neuilly*, provide sufficient detail for the technology to be copied today. Perronet's work is exceptional, being one of the few to show men at work on site.

Both Belidor and Perronet were also involved in teaching, the former at one of the military schools in the 1720s, while Perronet was involved in the establishment of the École des Ponts et Chaussées. Their work reflects the early emergence of the profession in France. The origins of this lead can be dated to the seventeenth century, and the vision of the ministers of the French monarchy of the time; Sully and Colbert in particular saw the advantages to France of a coordinated communications network as a basis for commercial prosperity. As early as 1599 Sully was given responsibility for France's roads, introducing a precept for roads and bridges the following year. Colbert appointed a Commissaire des Ponts et Chaussées in 1661, with engineers in charge of certain royal works being appointed as Inspecteurs des Ponts et Chaussées from 1668. It was not until the eighteenth century that they became engineers working exclusively in the state service, modelled on the military Corps du Génie established in 1676. This was formalized with the establishment of a Director-General with his Corps des Ponts et Chaussées in 1715. By this time the French engineers had embarked on a series of remarkable public works, the most famous being the Canal du Midi. In 1741 the civil 'Ponts et Chaussées' took over responsibility for ports, previously the province of the military. The final step towards the formation of a profession was the creation of an engineering school for the Corps des Ponts et Chaussées in 1747, modelled on the military schools established at Metz and elsewhere from 1689 onwards.

The French model was emulated first in Spain where a Director-General de Caminos y Canales was established in 1785, and later in Russia where the Institute of Ways and Communications was set up under French guidance in the Napoleonic period. Founded in 1809 to train Russian engineers, with a Corps of Engineers established in the following year, it continues today as the Institute of Railway Engineers in St Petersburg. French influence was most direct in Naples where Joseph Bonaparte established a school for the Corps degli Ingegneri di Ponti Estrade in 1811.

The idea of a central administration for roads, bridges and waterways was well-established elsewhere in central Europe, and from the late eighteenth century a system of technical education was established based on polytechnics (technical universities) rather than on a single élitist school. Examples of these are Berlin (Bauakademie, founded 1799), Prague (1806), Vienna (1815), Karlsruhe (1825). These developments were associated with the publication of a growing number of technical works to support the teaching programme such as Eytelwein's (Berlin) and Gerstner's (Prague). In the long term the continental system of education and training of engineers with an emphasis on sound theoretical understanding as the basis of engineering practice, rather than practical experience, was to prove an excellent foundation for advancing civil engineering in the second half of the nineteenth century.

A centralized bureaucracy and a rigid professional élite could, however, stifle innovation and institutionalize obsolescent technologies. There can be no doubt that by 1800 Great Britain had a tremendous technical lead over the rest of Europe, and at the close of the Napoleonic Wars a succession of continental civil engineers visited the British Isles to familiarize themselves with the latest developments in the structural use of iron, bridge construction, especially that of suspension bridges, dock construction, canals and, latterly, railways – Dupin, Dutens, Navier, Cordier (France); Kudriaffsky and Gerstner (Austria–Hungary); and Lentze (Prussia).

Our knowledge of British civil engineering practice at the time of its emergence as a distinct profession is based on a variety of surviving evidence. The most obvious is the extensive canal network, and its associated engineering works – overbridges, aqueducts, locks, tunnels, cuttings and embankments. Less obvious is the road network which was extensively improved in the eighteenth and early nineteenth centuries and remained the basis of the trunk-road network until the development of the motorway. A notable example is Thomas Telford's Holyhead Road, the basis

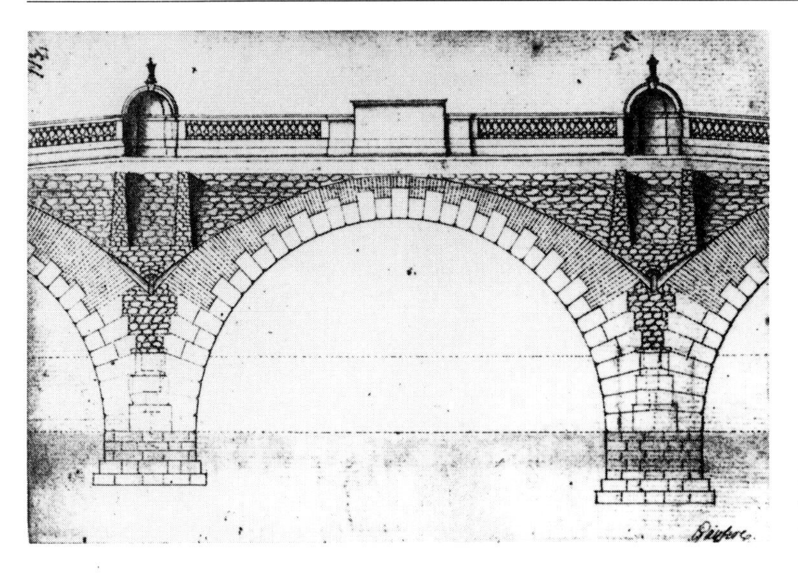

PLATE 13 Westminster Bridge, designed by Charles Labelye, was the first modern bridge across the Thames in London. Drawing by T. Gayfere, *c.* 1738

of the modern A5. Manuscript records also survive relating to the construction of many of these projects.

Our most extensive knowledge of eighteenth-century practice relates to John Smeaton, thanks in part to the survival of a remarkable number of his papers, and also due to the publication of his reports shortly after his death, under the auspices of the Smeatonian Society of Civil Engineers. Smeaton operated in a way similar to a modern consulting engineer. He would usually be consulted by local people to advise on a project, such as a bridge. He would submit a report, which would normally take the form of a letter, advising on the best location and potential problems, with alternative estimates, and a drawing – 'the rudest draft will explain visible things better than many words'.[1] Sometimes the report would be published, possibly to attract financial support for the scheme. The promoters of the scheme would then normally be expected to invite tenders for the construction of the work. The engineer might be asked to report on the tenders, and progress, but his involvement might cease with the original report. Work was usually carried out by local builders, and the general absence of detailed information in some reports makes it clear much reliance was placed on the contractors having the practical knowledge to carry out the works with a minimum of guidance.

With a canal scheme the situation was more complex. The engineer might engage the services of local surveyors to assist in the survey of the line and land valuation, as George Brown of Elgin did for the Caledonian Canal. The engineer would advise on the best line, likely engineering problems, costs of the scheme, and probable traffic and revenue. His services could be engaged to see the scheme through Parliament where he might meet opposition

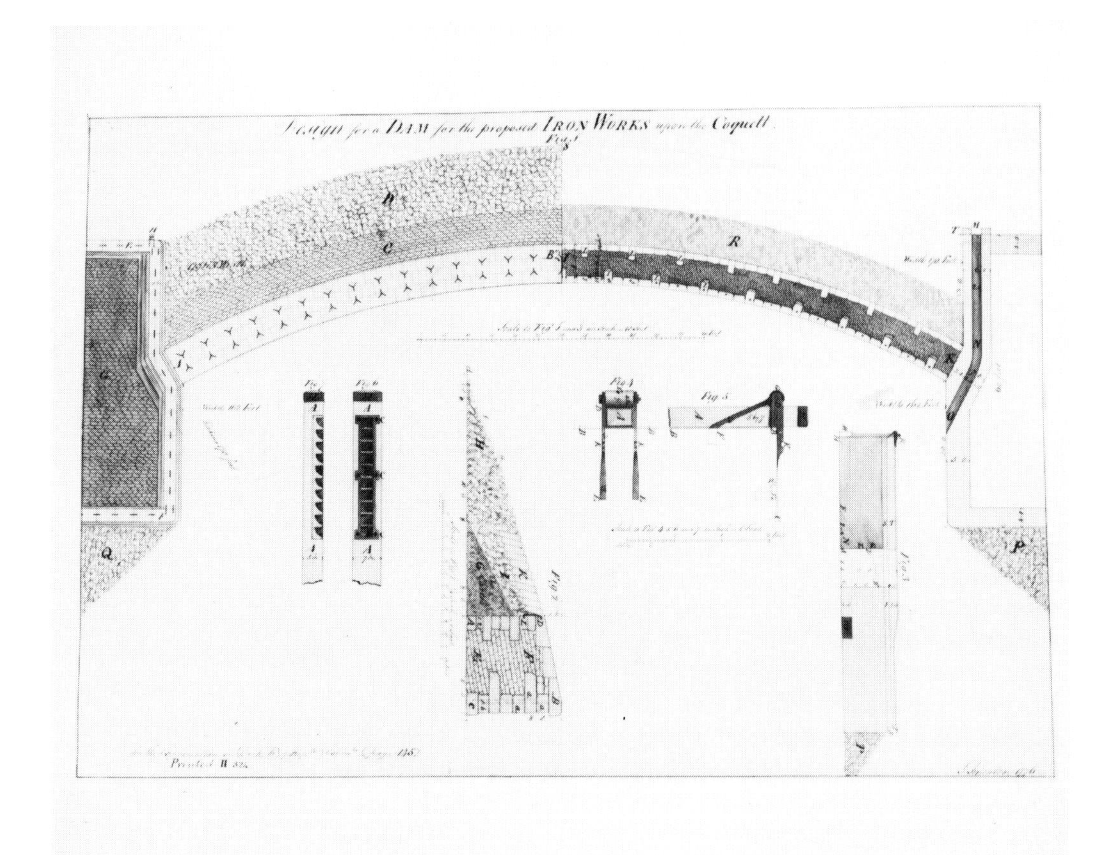

PLATE 14 Design for a dam for the proposed ironworks on the Coquet, 1776. Engineer: John Smeaton

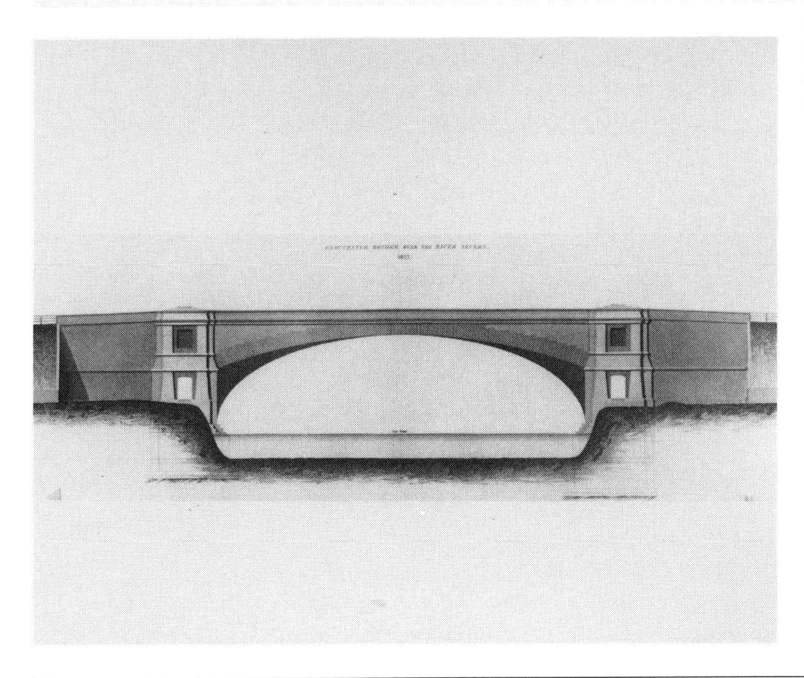

PLATE 15 Gloucester Bridge over the Severn, 1827. Engineer: T. Telford

from landed interest, and also engineers working for rival schemes or existing river navigations, who would seek to undermine his estimates and question his engineering judgement. If the scheme gained Parliamentary approval he might then be invited to supervise the works or recommend another engineer.

By the late eighteenth and early nineteenth centuries the practices of engineers like William Jessop, John Rennie, and Thomas Telford were so extensive it was impossible for them to supervise all their work personally. The best they could do was to try and visit all the works they were associated with, and concentrate on one or two major projects. To deal with this problem a resident engineer was normally appointed to take immediate charge of the works, and on a scheme like a canal he would increasingly call on the services of further assistants. Such a management structure had been advocated by Smeaton for the Forth Clyde Navigation in 1786.

The size and complexities of canal works meant that the use of a single local contractor was impossible, and the route was normally broken up into sections, and tenders invited for parts of the route, with major works such as aqueducts and large bridges often being advertised separately. Contractors could apply to the canal office for copies of the specification, and, if available, they could copy the drawings of the works, and would be expected to submit their tenders by a set date. Specifications were sometimes printed, but contained only a brief outline of the work involved, and a contractor would have needed some practical knowledge of civil engineering practice to draw up the quantities and adequately estimate the costs to ensure he tendered a reasonable price for the work. The successful contractor would be expected to be able to deposit a fixed sum, usually 10 per cent of the value of the contract, as an insurance against failure to complete the contract, and would need some financial guarantors such as local banks to support his financial solvency. As works progressed the client's representative, usually the resident engineer, would certify work done and authorize payment, which might be referred to the consultant. In the case of dispute over payment or carrying out the work, provision for an arbitrator would be made.

The weaknesses of the system were obvious. A canal company might be tempted to accept the lowest tender, with little regard to the competence of the contractor or the viability of his estimates. Smeaton attempted to persuade clients the lowest bid should not automatically be accepted. If a contractor had not foreseen a problem, such as hard rock or quicksand, he could rapidly hit financial problems as the rate of progress slowed down. If he had a sympathetic resident engineer he might be able to claim extra, but many contractors who hit a problem found it simpler to disappear. Even the most competent, such as Thomas Townshend, could be

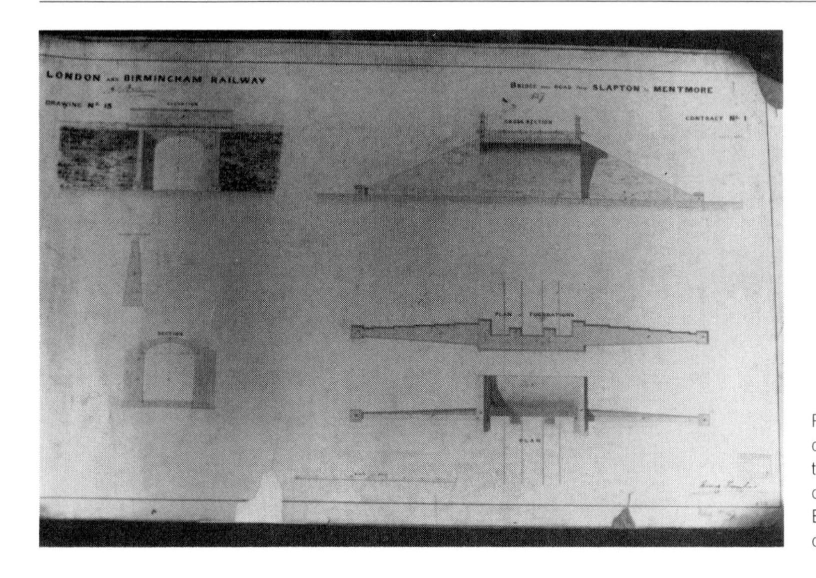

PLATE 16 Signed, pricked contract drawing for a bridge on the London–Birmingham Railway, over the Slapton–Mentmore road. Engineer: Robert Stephenson; contractor: T. Townshend

caught out, as he was on the Kilsby Tunnel on the London–Birmingham Railway. Unable to complete the works he was pursued through the bankruptcy courts although he was eventually able to discharge all his debts successfully.

Early contractors would generally have been local men, or as canal construction progressed an itinerant ganger with a barrow, but it is clear that by 1800 a group of competent men were emerging who could be relied upon to carry out work of a reasonable standard, who got their estimates right, could obtain financial backing because bankers and others realized they were likely to make a profit, and were trusted by engineers because of past performance. Thomas Telford is particularly well known for favouring certain contractors: William Hazledine for ironwork; John Simpson for masonry; etc. Other well-known contractors were Joliffe and Banks and Hugh McIntosh. The latter made the transition to railway work, as did William Mackenzie, who worked as a mason with his father before gaining invaluable experience as resident engineer under Telford on the Birmingham Canal. The contractor on the canal was Thomas Townshend, who was also to work on the railways. At the dawn of the railway age a contracting system had developed which was to prove capable of creating a transport revolution in Britain and abroad.

NOTE

1. Letter from John Smeaton, 1 August 1764 (Letter Book in ICE Archives).

CHAPTER THREE

What is Civil Engineering?

Bid harbours open, public ways extend,
Bid the broad arch the dangerous flood contain,
The mole projected break the roaring main,
Back to his bounds the subject sea command,
And roll obedient rivers through the land.
These honours peace to happy Britain brings,
These are imperial works, and worthy kings

Pope, Moral Essays, *Epist. iv, 197–204.*

By 1830, the dawn of the railway age, a mature profession existed in the British Isles with proven methods of organizing the construction of large projects, and an international reputation for technological innovation. It was a profession which would be recognized by the civil engineer of today, and whose leaders were well-known national figures. There are, however, important differences with today's profession. Put simply, a civil engineer then might embrace mechanical engineering, naval architecture, harbour engineering, bridge design and railway surveying in his practice. He was an engineer in the civil rather than the military sphere, and beyond that there was no limit to his practice. This is reflected in the original membership of the Institution of Civil Engineers.

Founded in 1818 by eight young engineers for 'facilitating the acquirement of knowledge requisite in their profession and for promoting mechanical philosophy',[1] the Institution contained only one member – Henry Robinson Palmer – who would probably be considered a civil engineer today, the remainder being the equivalent of modern mechanical engineers. The breadth of the professional interests of the membership were reflected in the definition of civil engineering provided by Thomas Tredgold for the first Charter (1828): '. . . the profession of a civil engineer, being the art of directing the great sources of power in Nature for the use and convenience of man.'

As the century progressed other engineering institutions were established, starting with the Institution of Mechanical Engineers in 1847. This reflects the growth in engineering specializations particularly associated with the development of the railway system, the introduction of iron shipbuilding powered by marine engines, and latterly the development of electric power. The Institution of Civil Engineers remained multidisciplinary in its membership throughout the period. Its meetings, the content of its publications, and the subject coverage of its library, all reflected a multidisciplinary profession. Leading members of the Institution were involved in the establishment of the new engineering societies which were encouraged by the Institution and offered their facilities for meetings. The Institution regarded itself as the senior professional body for all engineers, and this was reflected in the fact it was the only engineering body to have a Royal Charter.

PLATE 17 Sir Charles Fox, ironwork contractor and consulting engineer

In the period 1839–89 the dominant aspect of civil engineering, which above all others kept it in the public eye, and made the leaders of the profession public figures, was railway engineering. After the hesitant introduction of locomotive power on public railways, pioneered by George Stephenson in the 1820s, the success of the Liverpool and Manchester Railway led to an explosion of interest by investors, and a vast number of schemes were floated. These schemes provided employment for a whole range of people, some with only a tenuous link to the civil engineering profession previously. As Francis Roubiliac Conder, who served his engineering apprenticeship at the time, remarked, '. . . railways were the cry of the hour, and engineers were the want of the day. If they were not to be found ready made they had to be extemporised. And so they were . . . '.[2]

As construction progressed an enormous demand was created for a whole range of engineering products – locomotives and stationary engines, permanent way, stations and other structures and bridges. Although some of the railway schemes were quite modest, the scale of the largest projects required a degree of organization rarely seen before. On the London–Birmingham Railway Robert Stephenson developed a system which showed how it could be done (see Plate 16).

Stephenson realized the importance of a full survey and accurate drawings, to be able to monitor progress on the works and ensure quality control. As drawings were completed, a full description and specification were drawn up, and the contract could then be let. Contractors were paid monthly, with the resident engineer free to refer to the drawings and specifications to estimate the work done (see Plate 15). The line was divided into thirty divisions for letting as contracts, with one under Stephenson's direct supervision, the remainder being divided into four districts, under the superintendence of an assistant engineer, with three assistants.

In all, seventeen contractors were involved in the thirty contracts, Cubitt responsible for four and Nowells five. It was a masterpiece of organization.

The Stephenson model was copied by Brunel on the Great Western Railway. For the system to develop as rapidly as it did it required a degree of professional sophistication which became characteristic of the work of Joseph Locke in particular. Beginning with the Grand Junction Railway, Locke began to work with trusted contractors such as Thomas Brassey (see Plate 18) and William Mackenzie. The two firms combined to work overseas, beginning with France, with Locke as engineer on the first scheme – the Paris–Rouen–Le Havre Railway.

PLATE 18 Thomas Brassey, railway contractor. Carte-de-visite, 3.75 in x 2.25 in, by Moira and Haigh. Cartes-de-visite were invented by André Adolphe Disderi of Paris in 1854. They became very popular between 1860 and 1866 when people collected albums of portraits of famous people

The impact of the railways is hard to conceive today, but at the time Robert Stephenson attempted to quantify it in his Presidential Address to the Institution of Civil Engineers of 8 January 1856:

> At the end of 1854 . . . the aggregate length of railways opened in Great Britain and Ireland – measured about 8,054 miles – about the diameter of the globe, and nearly 500 miles more than the united lengths of the Thames, the Seine, the Rhône, the Ebro, the Tagus, the Rhine, the Elbe, the Vistula, the Dnieper, and the Danube, or the ten chief rivers of Europe . . . It will naturally be asked what amount of capital has been required for the construction of these vast works? . . . £286,000,000 has absolutely been raised. It is difficult to realise to the imagination what is £286,000,000 sterling. Let us try to test the importance of the amount by some familiar comparisons. It is more than four times the amount of the annual value of all the real property of Great Britain. It is more than one third of the entire amount of the National Debt . . . the expenditure of £286,000,000, by the people, has showed to us the advantages of internal communication, all but perfect – of progress in science and arts, unexampled at any period of the history of the world, – of National progress almost unchecked, and of prosperity and happiness, increased beyond all precedent . . . the magnitude of the railway-works undertaken in this country will be still more clearly exhibited if you consider the extent of the earthworks . . . they will measure 550,000,000 cubic yards . . . imagine a mountain half a mile in diameter at its base, and soaring into the clouds one mile and a half in height, – that would be the size of the mountain of earth which these earthworks would form; . . .[3]

Impressive as earthworks such as New Cross Cutting are, it is steam locomotives which are normally associated with the railway age. After a period of experimentation in the early 1830s locomotives began to adopt a form recognizable today.

PLATE 19 Glasgow Central station under construction, *c.* 1877. Engineer: Blyth & Blyth

PLATE 20 Locomotive type 91/82 on the Great Southern and Western Railway of Ireland. 11 in x 7 in. Engineer and photographer: J.A.F. Aspinall, *c.* 1882

As railway companies and locomotive works became established, characteristic designs emerged, and it is arguable that design became conservative. Many innovations such as those of Thomas Russell Crampton with cylinders and valve gear outside the wheels, were taken up on the Continent but largely ignored in the United Kingdom. One incentive to improvement was the interest in locomotive performance which was encouraged in the mid-1840s by the work of the Railway Gauge Commissioners comparing broad- and standard-gauge performance. On the Great Western Railway Daniel Gooch had been appointed locomotive superintendent in 1837. The early locomotives ordered by Brunel were unsatisfactory, and Gooch ordered a new series, modelled on Stephenson's *North Star*, known as the 'Firefly' class. They were very fast for the period, and while the Gauge Commissioners came down against the broad gauge, they concluded, 'broad gauge engines possess greater possibilities for speed with equal loads, and, generally speaking, of propelling greater loads with equal speeds'. Average speeds gradually increased from a best of 27 mph on the Liverpool–Manchester in the early 1830s to 43.7 mph on the London–Birmingham and 48.2 mph on the Great Western in 1845. In the 1870s Great Northern Railway expresses were averaging over 60 mph from King's Cross to Peterborough.

Locomotives were only one branch of steam-engine design with which civil engineers concerned themselves (see Plates 20, 58). Thousands of stationary steam engines were built, and were a considerable source of pride to the profession. Indeed, 'The steam engine . . . we may justly look upon as the noblest machine ever invented by man – the pride of the machinist, the admiration of the philosopher . . . '.[4] In the early development of the steam engine it had been almost exclusively used as a pumping engine. Even when it began to be used in factories it was to raise water to supplement water power. This severely limited its application. In the 1780s Watt and others developed rotative engines capable of driving mill machinery, in Watt's case by the use of a beam engine with parallel motion. By 1800 cast-iron beams and frames, slide valves, steam indicators, and governors had all become established features of steam-engine design, and in 1815 William Fairbairn introduced wrought-iron line shafts to transmit power from the machines.

For the next fifty years civil engineers developed boiler design and construction, enabling ever higher pressure engines to be used. By the 1830s average mill-engine pressure was *c.* 12 psi compared with 4–5 psi used by Watt, and the duty (number of pounds of water raised 1 foot through burning 1 bushel of coal) of engines increased from an average of 5.59 million lb in 1769 to 54 million lb in 1859. Refinement included compound (double cylinder) engines developed by Woolf 1803–14, and a variety of boilers such as the 'Cornish' and 'Lancashire'. The latter was introduced by William Fairbairn in the 1840s and had twin fire boxes.

These innovations made higher pressures possible, and required the use of wrought-iron plates and high-quality rivetting and were only made possible by improvements in iron working. To improve design British engineers began in the 1860s to borrow American ideas such as the Corliss engine, Allen valves, Porter governors, and Richards indicators. Horizontal engines began to replace beam engines, led by marine engines such as the trunk engines developed by John Penn in 1848 and used by the Admiralty. By 1870 it had replaced the beam engine for millwork. In the 1880s steam engines were being used to power electricity generators and in 1884 Charles Parsons patented his first steam turbine – developments which were to take this branch of engineering out of the hands of civil engineers in the next century.

Railway engineering brought together a variety of engineering skills which are today considered separate professions – civil and mechanical. Shipbuilding was another. In the early years of the nineteenth century marine steam engines and iron-hulled ships were being brought together for the first time. Early firms specializing in engines were those of Maudsley and Field – both founder members of the Institution of Civil Engineers, and John Penn, a member of ICE's Council and a founder member of the Institution of Mechanical Engineers. Progress in the use of iron and its combination with steam power was slow, and it was the early exponents of a new branch of engineering, naval architecture, who were able to demonstrate that this was the future for shipping.

John Wilkinson had built an iron hull as early as 1787 in

Coalbrookdale, and in 1822 the *Aaron Manby*, with an iron hull and steam power, had a successful trial on the Thames. However, it was not until Isambard Kingdom Brunel began to apply himself to the problems of ship design that the potential of the 'new' structural material iron, and steam power source came near realization. Brunel's first ship, SS *Great Western*, had a wooden hull, and was only slightly longer (236 ft against 226.5 ft) than HMS *Victory*. It was envisaged as an extension of the Great Western Railway from Bristol to New York. Its importance lay in demonstrating in 1838 the practicability of steamships crossing the Atlantic without the need to refuel. Brunel had held that the capacity of the hull of a ship increased with the cube of its dimensions, but the power, and thus the fuel needed, only increased with the square of its dimensions. Previously it had been widely believed that a vessel could not carry the fuel necessary for a transatlantic crossing, as the power required would increase with the cube of the dimensions.

Once Brunel became interested in the problems of ship design he would not let it go. The success of the SS *Great Western* encouraged the Great Western Steamship Company to commission a further steamship. Between 1839 and 1843 the SS *Great Britain* was built with an iron hull, as Brunel evolved methods of designing a large, iron ship capable of withstanding the rigours of a transatlantic crossing, and decided in favour of screw propulsion rather than paddle wheels.

Brunel correctly understood that a ship's design could be likened to that of a beam. He recognized the need for longitudinal stiffness. While working on the design of the SS *Great Eastern* he wrote, 'No materials shall be employed on any part except at the place and in the direction and in the proportion in which it is required and can be usefully applied for the strength of the ship . . . '.[5]

With the iron hull of the SS *Great Britain* he was able to use a wrought-iron cellular box structure, similar in cross section to that used in the tubular girders across the Conwy and Menai, to provide a double bottom and longitudinal stiffness in the hull. The general robustness of SS *Great Britain*'s design, with continuous iron cargo decks, and internal bracings and column supports, has helped ensure its survival to the present day.

Brunel's last ship, the SS *Great Eastern*, made greater use of this cellular arrangement, effectively providing a twin hull below the waterline, and a cellular upper deck to give additional strength against buckling. The use of standard size rivets and standardized plate thickness offered the potential of simplicity of fabrication, a feature which more than outweighed the overall increase in weight it involved. Despite such innovations the ship's construction became bedevilled with problems. In part they arose from the

PLATE 21 Steamhammer at Penn & Sons' works, *c.* 1860. From Barry, P., *Dockyard Economy and Naval Power*, London, Sampson Low, 1863. Barry's book contains the most comprehensive early collection of photographs of engineering workshops

PLATE 22 Bow of the *Great Eastern*, 2 November 1857, the day before the ship was christened. This first attempt to launch the *Leviathan*, as the ship was initially named, was unsuccessful. She was eventually launched using hydraulic rams on 31 January 1858. 14 in x 11 in. Photographer: R. Howlett, 1857

conflict between two men of genius: Brunel and John Scott Russell, the engineer entrusted with the vessel's construction. As construction proceeded, costs escalated. Problems of scale beset the project in its design, construction, launching, and finally at sea. While the practicability of building a ship on such a scale was demonstrated, it was ahead of its time; the traffic between Australia and Great Britain could not justify such a large vessel and the SS *Great Eastern* only saw thirty years' service. The SS *Great Eastern* was at its most successful when it was used for cable laying across the Atlantic and Indian Ocean in the late 1860s. Here the flexibility offered by the combination of paddle and screw propulsion came into its own.

The transatlantic telegraph is another example of the involvement of civil engineers in a branch of engineering which has since evolved as a separate profession – electrical engineering. The electric telegraph's widespread acceptance owed much to the railways. It was adopted along the London–Blackwall Railway to permit the safe working of the stationary engine system there, and its advantages were rapidly seized upon by Robert Stephenson and others. The first commercial public telegraph was run alongside the Great Western Railway from Paddington to West Drayton in 1839. Their close relationship with the safe working and management of railways ensured advances in electrical engineering remained an important topic for discussion at the Institution of Civil Engineers throughout the century.

The SS *Great Eastern* project marks the coming of age of another branch of civil engineering: naval architecture. Despite its problems this leviathan had demonstrated the advanced level of scientific knowledge and technology required to design and construct iron steamships successfully. In 1860 the (Royal) Institution of Naval Architects was founded, with John Scott Russell taking the lead. Naval architecture, perhaps more clearly than any other branch of civil engineering, was a proving ground for new ideas. At a time when structural engineering did not exist as a distinct branch, naval architects were combining a new structural material – iron – and a new method of propulsion – steam – in a hostile environment where failure meant death. Brunel, Russell, and others were able to challenge centuries of tradition partly by an engineer's feel for the materials involved, and partly by a scientific approach to the 'new' problems they faced. As a consequence of the revolution in shipbuilding there was a continual cross-fertilization of ideas and experience between those in the shipyards, and others in the civil engineering mainstream of railways.

A prime example of this is to be found in the career of William Fairbairn. His Millwall shipbuilding yard was bought out by John Scott Russell and used for the SS *Great Eastern*. In the same yard

PLATE 23 Palm House, Kew, under construction, 1847. This is possibly the earliest British example of photography of a structure under construction. Engineer: R. Turner; daguerreotype: A.F.J. Claudet

many of the tests for the form of the Britannia Bridge had been carried out in the mid-1840s. The skills required in the fabrication of plate girder and tubular girder bridges were similar to those required in the shipyards, with their needs for top-quality rivetting to join boiler plates together. Earlier Fairbairn had been involved in millwork, and the erection of multi-storey textile mills, in whose design lay the origins of modern steel-frame structures.

Naval architecture and the associated marine engineering in many ways represented the leading edge of civil engineering at this time. The demands of high-pressure boilers, fluid loading and practical fabrication led to the development of new ideas and practices which were taken up elsewhere. To take one unlikely example, the wrought-iron rib construction which gives the Palm House at Kew its graceful form was made possible by using Vernon and Kennedy's patent beam for ships' decks. It took the skill of Dublin ironfounder Richard Turner to realize this could be utilized to form the basis of the glasshouse structure, by thermic welding of the 3.8 m beams into 12 m lengths. This structure provides one of the clearest examples of the need for architects, in this case Decimus Burton, to call on the expertise of engineers in the design of structures which required non-conventional uses of structural materials.

The importance of the engineer is also seen in Crystal Palace, often seen as a Victorian triumph of glass and iron. Although the original design was the idea of Sir Joseph Paxton, a landscape gardener with a gift for glasshouse architecture, it could only have been built as a result of a mature civil engineering industry exhibiting a whole range of skills acquired over the previous century. Its construction made extensive use of timber, glass and iron, and the swift progress from design through construction to completion in nine months is a tribute to the skills of the main contractors, Fox Henderson of Birmingham. They had developed considerable expertise in the design and construction of large-span iron structures in the naval dockyards, and some of the more important early railway stations such as London Euston, the first to have an iron roof over its train shed. They were able to replicate some of the details from these structures in Crystal Palace, and the use of standardized designs enabled them to produce a structure which could readily be prefabricated, transported, assembled, and ultimately taken down and re-erected.

Prefabrication had by now become a necessary feature of civil engineering as the use of metals expanded. Prefabricated steam engines had been sent in parts around the country by Boulton and Watt. Early iron bridges such as Bonar and Craigellachie in Scotland had been cast in parts in Shropshire by William Hazledine before being shipped and finally transported overland to their erection sites. Ironfounders eager for mass markets began to develop prefabricated buildings for export to the colonies. The 1851 Exhibition building provides the most illustrious example of this branch of the industry.

The civil engineering achievements of the period took place against a background of increased theoretical understanding of the processes involved. They were also backed up by continuing research and testing. The earliest engineering textbooks like Belidor and Barlow devoted a considerable amount of space to properties of materials. Guides for use in buildings and bridges were frequently tested both at the manufacturers and on site. The problem for the engineer in assessing the various published results, and indeed any he might conduct himself, was the absence of standardization in test procedures or specimens, which made comparison and validity of results difficult to assess.

In 1858 David Kirkaldy attempted to solve these problems by developing a lever testing machine to test iron and steel for boilers and marine engines at Robert Napier's works in Glasgow. He meticulously recorded the methodology and results of his tests, which were completed in 1861. While carrying out the work he clearly appreciated its value to the engineering profession gen-

PLATE 24 Great Exhibition building, Hyde Park, West End, 1851. 8.25 in x 6.5 in, from a salt paper print. Engineer: Fox Henderson; photographers: Hugh Owen/C.M. Ferrier

erally, and resolved to make a career of it. He designed and patented a testing machine capable of testing all types of material, subjected to all manner of stresses. Kirkaldy moved to London and established his works in Southwark in 1865. The results of his tests were reproduced in all the standard textbooks and engineering manuals for the next fifty years. Among his more famous commissions were the tests he carried out on the specimens from the failed Tay Bridge. Notwithstanding such failures, bridge engineering probably provides the clearest examples of the application of research and theory to practice in the Victorian era.

NOTES

1. Resolution of 13 January 1818, ICE Minute book, no. 1, p. 14.
2. F.R. Conder, *Personal recollections of English engineers*, 1868, p. 46.
3. ICE *Minutes of Proceedings*, vol. 15, pp. 124–5.
4. M.A. Alderson, 'An essay on the nature and application of steam', 1834.
5. I.K. Brunel, Private Letter-book, 26 February 1854.

CHAPTER FOUR

The Sappers – Civil Engineers in all but Name?

Engineer, in the military art, properly denotes, an able, expert man, who by a perfect knowledge in mathematics, delineates upon paper, or marks upon the ground, all sorts of forts and other works proper for offence and defence.

Hinde, A New Royal and Universal Dictionary, *1769.*

If one wants to view the range of interests of Victorian engineers one has to go no further than the photographic work of the Royal Engineers (see Plates 25, 26, 27 and 28). The photographs themselves bear witness to three facets of the professional work of military engineers of the time: a scientific training which enabled them to master the new art; an innovative approach to new problems which enabled them to meet the various challenges set them by successive governments; and, most obviously, the fact much of their time was spent in a civil rather than military context.

Despite the apparent split between the civil and military branches of engineering, there was in fact a healthy exchange of information and technology between the two spheres. The experience of military engineers had already played its role in shaping the civil profession. The military engineers were called upon to play an important role in the civil sphere by governments who lacked alternative research facilities, lacked impartial advisers in the face of competing commercial interests, and in particular, they lacked people of sufficient expertise to construct the infrastructure essential to colonial development overseas.

Military engineers had, unlike most of their civil counterparts, the benefit of some formal engineering education at the Royal Military Academy, and latterly the Royal Engineers Establishment at Chatham. A succession of excellent textbooks was produced by General Pasley on cements, fortification and practical

PLATE 25 Re-erection of Woolwich No. 4 slip roof at Chatham Dockyard, *c.* 1876. The flexibility of these large-span iron shipyard roofs was demonstrated by the ease with which they could be transported and re-erected, as was done with several of the Woolwich buildings in the 1870s. Engineers: Colonel Brandreth/Fox Henderson; contractor: Fox Henderson (1847)

architecture, Douglas on military bridges, and Barlow on strength of materials. These all reflected the state of engineering knowledge of the time, based on a broad range of reading and practical knowledge. As the century progressed the papers published by the Corps of Royal Engineers, and their Indian equivalents, recorded the work of the engineers, including research and construction work, much of a civil nature. In the 1860s and '70s lectures on the pattern of those at the École des Ponts et Chaussées were given by leading engineers and scientists at Chatham, including guest speakers such as W.C. Unwin.

One example where the military and civil branches of the profession met was in railway engineering. In the 1830s, concern over the safety of the new means of transport, and the need for impartial advice on schemes, led the Government to call on Royal Engineers to advise on railways, and inspect new lines and structures prior to their opening. They were also employed to report on all accidents, a function which remains to this day. The civil engineers often resented this interference, regarding the military as a conservative influence with no real understanding of the civil engineer's methods.

An early example of the conflict was provided with the inspectorate's initial refusal to approve the Torksey tubular girder bridge designed by John Fowler in 1849. This decision was criticized at

PLATE 26 Interior of the 1862 London Exhibition building. Engineer: Captain F. Fowke; contractor: Kelk & Lucas; photographer: C.T. Thompson (J.G. James Collection)

the Institution of Civil Engineers. While one can sympathize with the inspecting engineer's reluctance to approve an innovative structure whose design he apparently imperfectly understood, this did not prevent other sappers approving the Dee and Tay bridges, both notorious failures based on conventional designs.

Elsewhere the sappers were themselves involved in some of the most innovative engineering work of the nineteenth century. Their place in the military hierarchy made them an obvious source of expertise in the naval dockyards. Here concern over the ravages of dry rot in the Napoleonic Wars had led to a change from constructing wooden ships in the open to covering them with building slips with wide-span roofs, initially of timber. As ships grew larger so did the demand for larger span roofs, and between 1844 and 1857 sixteen wide-span iron structures were built. Most of these were designed and built by the contractors Fox Henderson and George Baker and Sons, but the Royal Engineers seem to have been responsible for the decision to introduce iron under Colonel Brandreth, Director of the Admiralty Works Department

PLATE 27 Royal Albert Hall, *c.* 1866. Engineers: General Scott, Captain Fowke; ironwork contractor: Fairbairns; general contractor: Lucas (J.G. James Collection)

from 1837, and military engineers were involved in the supervision of all the work.

Most distinguished of the engineers who worked in this sphere was Colonel Godfrey Thomas Greene, successor to Brandreth from 1850. He designed a slip roof at Chatham, developing Fox Henderson's designs, and subsequently the boat store at Sheerness, the world's first free-standing, multi-storey, iron-framed building. This was erected by Grissells between 1858 and 1860, some thirty years before the Chicago School used the system as the basis of the modern skyscraper.

The work in the dockyards was still very much in a military context. This was hardly the case with the sappers' work in South Kensington. While the first South Kensington museum building, the Kensington Gore museum (erected 1856-7), was maligned as the Brompton Boilers, and had few architectural pretensions, the Royal Albert Hall was regarded as a masterpiece of architecture, the engineering input almost completely overshadowed.

The 'Brompton Boilers' were erected under the superintendence of Sir William Cubitt by the iron manufacturers C.D. Young and Company, who had considerable expertise in prefabricated building. Its external austerity was due in part to the extensive use of corrugated iron cladding, originally patented by Henry Robinson Palmer, founder of the Institution of Civil Engineers, in 1829. The museum was only intended as a short-term solution to the need to house the growing number of exhibits for the Board of Trade's Department of Practical Art. As work progressed Captain Francis Fowke was brought in to superintend the building of the museum and work on the design of the permanent structures. While a final design was decided upon, Fowke started with picture galleries, followed by a conservatory for the Royal Horticultural Society (1861) and roofs for the courts of the South Kensington museum. In the 1862 Exhibition building he designed 160 ft diameter 250 ft high domes, relying on the assistance of the civil engineers J.W. Grover and John Fowler, producing a structure very reminiscent of the railway stations of the time. Fowke was working on designs for the Royal Albert Hall when he died in December 1865. Henry Cole remarked of him '. . . to my mind [he] was solving the problem of the decorative use of iron, and by appreciating the spirit both of the Gothic and Renaissance architects, was on the threshold of introducing a novel style of architecture . . . '.[1]

Fowke's place was taken by General Scott, under whose authority several important design changes were made, whereby the hall was altered from one with two semi-circular ends and two parallel sides to an ellipse. Engineering advice was available from Sir John Fowler and John Hawkshaw, who were on the Advisory Committee, and, for detailed design from Grover and R.M. Ordish. The dome roof used many of the details of the ironwork of the civil engineering structures of the time. The principals were wrought-iron trussed girders reflecting the design of Hawkshaw's near contemporary (1866) Cannon Street station roof, with other details from the much earlier (1854) Birmingham New Street station on which Ordish had worked. Ironwork was supplied by Fairbairn's, and Sir William Fairbairn further modified some of the details. Such a collaboration between the civil and military branches of the profession was typical of the time.

Of particular help to civil engineers were the tests carried out at times by the military. One of the earliest textbooks for civil engineers, Peter Barlow's work on strength and stress of timber (1817), contained the results of his tests on timber at the Royal Arsenal and Woolwich Dockyard. His objective was to 'put the practical engineer in possession of certain facts . . . and several rules for computation that he will in vain look for in any other work.'[2] Barlow had the resources to carry out his experiments which were rarely available to his civilian colleagues at the time, although his work also contains results of contemporary tests by Telford and others in civilian factories. Such was Barlow's success that his work was reprinted many times, with additions, over

PLATE 28 Demolition of Rochester Bridge, 1856–7. Photographer: Sergeant Dukes

the following fifty years. Colonel Pasley was responsible for research into limes and cements, as well as bringing together a summary of much earlier work. In a more obviously military context in 1842–3 Lieutenant Hope carried out some of the earliest British experiments on earth pressure and full-scale model retaining walls. These supported the use of battered walls as developed by engineers in the London dock schemes earlier in the century.

With the engineering advances in the civil sphere in the Victorian era, the military freely borrowed the expertise of their civil colleagues even in their own field. The introduction of steam-powered ironclads threatened to render the Royal Navy obsolescent and made it imperative all available advice should be sought on the development of an iron-clad Navy. The first modern warship to be built for the navy was the *Warrior*. After its completion an advisory committee was set up including the leading naval architects, and a variety of iron-clad armour designs were tried out, including that of the *Warrior*.

Just as the military used civil expertise in their sphere, civil engineers used the military to assist in civil work. In 1856–7 the

Royal Engineers were asked to assist in the demolition of the old Rochester Bridge by the use of explosives. This was the first civil engineering job undertaken by the sappers for which they took record photographs.

NOTES

1. H. Cole, Corps of Royal Engineers, *Professional papers on subjects connected with the duties of the Corps, New Series*, 1866, vol. xv, p. xv.
2. P. Barlow, *An Essay on the strength and stress of timber*, 1817, Preface.

CHAPTER FIVE

Bridges

'There are few operations of art in which mankind are more deeply interested than in what relates to bridges. The ingenuity and hazard involved in constructing them; the numerous advantages derived from them; their being from objects of utility, in many instances, raised into all the magnificence which science and power can exalt them; justify us in treating the subject at considerable length, and endeavouring to exhibit under one article, most of the material circumstances which are connected with it.'

Thomas Telford, Edinburgh Encyclopedia, *volume 4, 1830, written 1812.*

A bridge, regardless of form, is an ideal symbol of civil engineering. Its design and construction combine almost all the essential components of modern civil engineering: transport engineering, whether road or rail; hydraulic engineering, with regard to scour and the bridge waterway; geotechnics, for the design of the foundations and abutments; structural analysis and design, to select its form and dimensions; materials science, to correctly specify the materials; construction technology, to ensure the safe erection of a structure over an open space; and environmental engineering, to ensure an harmonious design for the location.

The first fifty years of photography coincided with the most frenetic period of bridge building in the history of the British Isles. In 1838 there were approximately 22,000 miles of turnpike road in Britain and £46,000 was spent on bridges by county authorities. In the same year thirty-seven railway schemes were before Parliament, many involving crossing this same network many times. Between 1839 and 1889 more than 19,000 route miles of railway had been built. This involved more than 25,000 bridges by the end of 1854. The majority of these bridges were designed and built using methods which had been developed over preceding centuries, and more particularly during the development of the canal network and improvement of roads over the previous fifty years.

PLATE 29 Leven Viaduct, Forth–Clyde Railway, *c.* 1867. This forms one of a series of photographs taken for the Caledonian Railway to demonstrate the incompetence of the Forth Clyde Company. 14.75 in x 8.75 in. Engineer: Charles Jopp; photographer: A. Crowe

Most of these bridges were built using traditional methods and materials, and it is the scale of the achievement, rather than the method which inspires most wonder today.

The largest proportion of the bridge spans were masonry, using locally quarried stone, or bricks fired nearby or on site, according to material availability and price. The problem of the oblique crossing of roads or waterways had been solved by William Chapman in Ireland in the canal age, and was again overcome by George Stephenson at Rainhill. After causing a flurry of interest in the literature of the late 1830s, such bridges became commonplace. Under normal circumstances the tried combination of multiple spans of masonry and mortar erected on timber centering during erection, was a preferable expedient to the pursuit of wider spans of other material, unless navigation or other interests dictated otherwise.

Aside from masonry the other traditional construction material used in railway bridges was timber. Although timber bridges had a long history in Britain, the early London Bridge crossings for example, it was not widely used. Concerns about its durability in the British climate, and the ravages of Britain's Navy on the native forests meant that a tradition of innovative timber design had not developed as it had in central Europe. The railway age offered a revival of interest in timber bridges. Brunel in particular made use of the material, and carried out tests on its strength and durability after preservative treatment. His most famous structures were a series of more than fifty viaducts on lines in Devon and Cornwall. Timber was partly chosen for its lower capital cost, accepting there would be a need for maintenance, but hoping this could be financed out of revenue once the lines were open. The bridges were designed with maintenance in mind, but within fifty years almost all had been replaced by masonry arches. Although described as timber, they contained substantial amounts of other materials: most had masonry piers, wrought-iron ties and cast-iron shoes for the timber elements. Brunel used timber elsewhere on all his lines: Landore Viaduct on the South Wales Railway, and a skew bridge over the Avon at Bath. The latter was a laminated arch bridge, and although it was Brunel's only use of the technique it was used elsewhere by British railway engineers.

The laminated arch was pioneered in Bavaria by Wiebeking in 1807–9. It was introduced into Britain by John Green for the Ouseburn and Willington viaducts on the Newcastle and North Shields Railway and was subsequently used by leading engineers such as Charles Blacker Vignoles and Joseph Locke, and lesser-known figures such as Robertson and Valentine. Locke used laminated arches on his Paris–Rouen–Le Havre Railway, and used other forms of timber bridge elsewhere where it was convenient. Generally, however, timber was not widely adopted.

By the 1830s the use of iron in bridges could be considered traditional. Nearly fifty years had elapsed since the erection of the Iron Bridge at Coalbrookdale and although in the eighteenth century relatively few successful applications followed, by 1830 iron was a well-tried material for canal and road bridges. Many spans were modest but both engineers and ironmasters were familiar with the concept, and happy to use such structures. The typical form was a cast-iron arch, which made best use of cast iron's compressive strength, although beam, swing, suspension and truss bridges had all been tried by the end of the decade.

The least successful form had proved to be suspension bridges, which, as then designed, proved incapable of withstanding dynamic railway loads. Of the first, over the Tees on the Stockton–Darlington Railway, Robert Stephenson remarked, 'Immediately on opening the undulations into which the roadway was thrown, by the inevitable unequal distribution of the weight of the train upon it, were such as to threaten the instant downfall of the whole structure.'[1]

Iron truss bridges had been used since the Gaunlees Bridge on the Stockton–Darlington Railway (1825) which apparently used, in a crude sense, the compressive strength of cast iron and tensile strength of wrought iron to provide a satisfactory design. Telford had developed aesthetically pleasing arch bridge designs in the 1810s at Bonar and elsewhere, but an arch design was not always satisfactory. It was desirable to maximize headroom to provide openings for navigation or road traffic without unnecessarily raising the level of the railway, which added expense in terms of earthworks or locomotives working on gradients. The arch form restricted headroom at all except mid-span. In contrast beam bridges were ideal, but longer spans were impractical without some sort of truss to support the deck. In addition large castings for arches were known to carry an inherent danger of blow holes, caused by imperfect manufacture, which would disastrously weaken the structure. Against this background, and with a host of manufacturers competing for business, a miscellany of iron bridges was used in the early days of the railways as dependable structural forms were evolved.

One attempt at solving the problem of longer spans was the trussed beam or compound girder. This attempted to make possible longer-span iron bridges by combining lengths of cast-iron beams and strengthening them with wrought-iron ties. Such girders were used in bridges from 1831. In 1847 such a span, 108 ft long, failed over the River Dee, shortly after a trussed beam in a cotton mill in Oldham had collapsed. The resultant furore severely damaged the reputation of Robert Stephenson, engineer for the Dee Bridge, and demonstrated the need to develop alternative methods of iron bridge construction. The timing coincided with a demand for longer-span bridge crossings, as the railways had developed sufficiently to overcome most of the simpler natural obstacles, and were left with a number of wider spans to cross to complete the main network. As a result, in the late 1840s British engineers carried out some of the most important research in the history of civil engineering, in an attempt to develop safe designs for railway bridges.

The most important crossing, responsible for much of this work, was that of 1,511 ft across the Menai Straits, for the Chester–Holyhead Railway. With similar Admiralty restrictions faced by Thomas Telford a generation earlier when designing the Menai crossing for the Holyhead Road, Robert Stephenson, engineer for the railway, initially thought a suspension bridge would have to be built. Problems with the earlier suspension railway bridge over the Tees persuaded Stephenson that a substantial girder would have to be developed to stiffen the structure, and therefore he called on the expertise of William Fairbairn, who conducted a series of tests on various types of wrought-iron girders. Fairbairn in turn made use of Eaton Hodgkinson, who had already been responsible for much research into the properties of iron, and had a good grasp of the theory of structures. The result of the research was to demonstrate that rectangular tubes of wrought iron, stiffened by a cellular arrangement, were capable of spanning the Straits without the need for suspension chains.

In addition to Fairbairn and Hodgkinson, Stephenson called on the expertise of other leading scientists and engineers, such as Henry Moseley, William Pole and Charles Head Wild, to assist in analysing the revolutionary structure, and check the stresses and strains it was supposed to bear. Above all Stephenson had the services of Edwin Clark as resident engineer. Clark had sufficient scientific understanding to calculate the stresses involved in the erection of the bridge, and its 400 ft span twin at Conwy, and was responsible for managing safe erection. Menai was erected in four sections, two land spans of 230 ft, and two navigation spans of 460 ft, supported on a central pier founded on Britannia Rocks, from which the bridge takes its name. The two main spans were floated out and then lifted into position using hydraulic jacks. When the four sections were in position the tubes were slightly raised and lowered in turn to close the joints, and rivetted together to form a beam continuous across all the supports. This method of erection minimized the maximum bending moment due to the self-weight of the bridge. Such sophistication proves the error of any suggestion that British engineers avoided theory in their practice.

Britannia Bridge excited the attention of the world engineering community unlike any structure of its time. While criticism was levelled at its uneconomic use of material compared with various truss designs, the intellectual effort involved in its design and construction was, and remains, a source of wonder. This research formed the basis for a variety of structural engineering developments increasingly remotely removed from the tubular girder itself. Although only a handful of tubular bridges were ever built, box girders continue to be used to this day. Following on from the Britannia research came a whole variety of bridges, mostly using plate girders, although tubular girder bridges used cellular girders rather than built-up plate sections for their main structural support.

Stephenson called on his contemporary Brunel for support and advice on the Britannia Bridge. This was reciprocated when Brunel designed his rivals to the Britannia Bridge, the Chepstow Bridge over the Wye and the Saltash Bridge over the Tamar. Both of these made use of wrought-iron tubes, but Brunel preferred to use oval tubes to suspend the plate girders supporting the track rather than constructing massive tubes through which the trains could run. The Royal Albert Bridge, Saltash, can be seen as the culmination of Brunel's bridge design work. Stephenson's bridge had few direct emulators, and Brunel's had none, but the contribution of the research after Britannia to the development of structural engineering is clear, while Saltash seems only to demonstrate Brunel's unique genius. The overall length of Saltash was nearly 2,200 ft. The two main spans of 455 ft comprised giant trusses with parabolic-arched wrought oval tubes tied by two pairs of suspension chains. The trusses were divided into panels by

PLATE 30 Britannia Bridge under construction, 1849. Engineer: Robert Stephenson; contractor: C.J. Mare

vertical members from which the deck was suspended. The bridge took three and a half years to build, with the main construction problem being the caisson foundation for the central pier, which had to be floated into position and sunk before work on the superstructure could begin.

While Brunel and Stephenson completed these designs for their major bridges, other engineers were using simpler and more economic solutions to develop girder bridges. At their simplest they took the form of triangular trusses of the Warren type, introduced to the Continent by an Englishman, A.H. Neville, in the 1840s, before their first use in this country at Joiner Street under London Bridge station in 1850. These bridges in their classic form used cast iron in compression and wrought iron in tension. Notable examples were the 240 ft 6 in span Newark Dyke Bridge on the Great Northern Railway, and the Crumlin Viaduct in South Wales, at 200 ft the tallest viaduct on British Railways until its demolition in the 1960s. Engineers found it easy to analyse the

PLATE 31 The construction of Royal Albert Bridge, Saltash, 1857. 10.5 in x 8.25 in. Engineer: I.K. Brunel; contractors: C.J. Mare/ Hudson & Male; photographer: Roger Fenton; printer: Cundall & Downes

strains in this type of bridge, and it was particularly popular for the export market. Other iron truss bridges evolved, more closely resembling timber forms adopted from American practice. The earliest such bridges appear to have been the Rahery Road (1843) and Royal Canal (1845) bridges on the Dublin–Drogheda Railway. Their close-lattice structure resembled the American Town truss. Some were straightforward copies, such as the Pratt truss used for the Charing Cross Railway Bridge, but many were double or treble Warren trusses, the number of triangulations being related to length of span and desired strength. Throughout the 1850s and '60s arguments persisted over the most economic form of girder for a given span. By the mid-1860s Benjamin Baker had concluded that the most economic form for long-span bridges was the cantilever.

The engineer who built his reputation on his economic form of bridge designs was Thomas Bouch. In the north of England he was responsible for a series of viaducts such as that at Belah whose slenderness of form and economic use of material made him popular in the railway boardrooms. In his calculations he was assisted by an Edinburgh consultant, R.H. Bow, and by 1870 his

PLATE 32 View of the Tay Bridge following its failure in 1879. This view demonstrates the inadequacy of the anchorages for the columns, which were only carried down through two courses of masonry, a method of construction which proved totally inadequate for the wind loads of 28 December 1879. Engineer: T. Bouch; contractor: Hopkins Gilkes & Company

reputation was so high that he was submitting designs for the great spans across the Scottish estuaries of the Tay and Forth.

Work began on the Tay Bridge in 1871. For the navigation spans it comprised thirteen wrought-iron triangulated through trusses, eleven of 245 ft span, two of 227 ft, supported on cast-iron columns on masonry piers. These were approached by eighty-five wrought-iron lattice girder spans. On its completion in 1878 it was the longest railway viaduct in the world. Unfortunately it was destroyed in a gale on 29 December the following year, while a train was crossing. The failure of the bridge and the consequent loss of seventy-five lives finished Bouch's career. Failure was due to a combination of poor workmanship, both in the original fabrication of the cast-iron columns and the erection of the bridge, and inadequate design. The subsequent inquiry revealed that insufficient attention had been paid to wind loading, and regulations were changed to take account of wind loads for subsequent bridges. The replacement viaduct, 10,527 ft long and designed by William Henry Barlow, was generally a much more substantial structure, founded on seventy-three pairs of wrought-iron cylinders, and was opened on 20 June 1887.

More or less contemporaneously with the original Tay Bridge the River Severn was being spanned further south. The Severn Railway Bridge was built partly to serve Sharpness Docks and the Forest of Dean coalfield. It crossed the Severn at Sharpness, and was 4,161 ft long, including the masonry approach viaduct. Cast-iron piers were sunk by means of compressed air through the estuarine sand to the rock below, sometimes at a depth of 76 ft. The superstructure comprised twenty-one wrought-iron bowstring

PLATE 33 Severn Railway Bridge under construction, 1879. 10.5 in x 8 in. Engineer: T.E. Harrison; contractor: Windsor Iron Works, Liverpool; photographer: G.W. Keeling (in the centre of the photograph)

girders, the two largest being of 327 ft span. There was also a swing span over the Gloucester–Berkeley Canal. One unusual feature of the bridge's construction was the decision to put the girders together on site on timber staging rather than floating prefabricated girders out and lifting them using hydraulic presses. The consultant, T.E. Harrison, appears to have been concerned that the current in the river would have been too strong for the lifting to have been carried out safely. Work on the bridge began in March 1875, and it was opened in October 1879.

Of particular interest is the series of photographs taken by G.W. Keeling, resident engineer on the bridge (see Plates 1, 33). Prior to the construction of the Forth Bridge these form the most complete photographic record of bridge construction in the British Isles.

The Forth Railway Bridge is the achievement of arguably the greatest British civil engineering partnership of the second half of the nineteenth century – Sir John Fowler and Sir Benjamin Baker – and unlike many other nineteenth-century landmarks of British civil engineering, it survives intact to bear witness to an age of great engineers. From the first the structure seized the imagination

PLATE 34 Forth Railway Bridge under construction, 23 July 1888, showing temporary bracing and access platforms on cantilevers. Engineers: Sir John Fowler and Sir Benjamin Baker; contractor: Tancred Arrol; photographer: P. Phillips

of artists, and it was extensively photographed and otherwise recorded. The result is that we have a better idea today of how the bridge was constructed than possibly any other structure of its time.

The engineers responsible for the design already had distinguished careers behind them and international reputations. Fowler was at forty-nine the youngest ever President of the Institution of Civil Engineers (in 1866). He later wrote, 'Before I was nineteen I was a good engineering surveyor and leveller, could set out works, and measure them up for certificates to be paid to contractors.'[2] Already established in private practice, Fowler moved to London in 1844, as consultant to three railway schemes. In 1862 Fowler was working on the Metropolitan and District Railways and Baker joined as his pupil and was assigned to these projects. In 1866 Baker wrote a series of articles in *Engineering* on 'Long Span Bridges'. Later published in book form, both in the United Kingdom and overseas, it reveals that Baker and Fowler regarded cantilever bridges (or as Baker described them, 'continuous girders of varying depth') as the most suitable for long spans.

The Forth had always been a barrier to the east of Scotland, necessitating either a ferry crossing or long journey via Stirling for anybody wishing to travel north from Edinburgh. In 1805 a tunnel scheme was proposed, and in 1818, in the first rush of enthusiasm for the 'new' structural form, a suspension bridge. From the 1860s, with the development of the railway network, more serious proposals were advanced.

In 1873 the Forth Bridge Railway Company was established to build Thomas Bouch's second proposal (the first in 1865 having failed after financial problems) for a suspension bridge of 2,000 ft spans. Although work began, and a brick pier was built by Arrols on Inch Garvie, an island in the estuary, activity was suspended following the failure of the Tay Bridge and Bouch's reputation.

The way was now open for Fowler and his team. Leading engineers William H. Barlow, John Fowler and Thomas E. Harrison were asked to consider a new design for a bridge or tunnel crossing. In 1881 Fowler and Baker's cantilever proposal, modified by Barlow and Harrison, was approved by the directors and in 1882 the Act of Parliament passed.

The design was dictated by 'economy of material and facility of erection' (B. Baker).[3] A continuous girder of varying plan and section was the basis of the design. No untried materials were used. Although this was the first large-scale use of structural steelwork in Britain, Fowler and Baker felt its value had already been proven and indeed believed their design was not possible without it. The compression members were steel tubes up to 12 ft diameter, tests having already proven it was the strongest form inch for inch.

Baker devised a human cantilever to illustrate the principle of the design in his lectures on the scheme. The objective of the design was maximum rigidity. The fixed ends of the cantilever were weighted to balance half the weight of the central girder and a train load. To balance the central (Inch Garvie) pier its base was extended as far as possible. Bed plates facilitated movement and only one of the four skew backs was fixed to each pier. The direct effect of the sun, thermal effects, and wind loads were all allowed for in the design with expansion joints, sliding bed plates and bracing.

On 21 December 1882 the contract was awarded to Tancred Arrol and Company, Arrol having been the original contractor for the bridge. The site selected for the bridge was the narrowest part of the Forth, with the depth of water well within the capacity of pneumatic caissons.

In December 1882 Arrol's original workshops were taken over, the baseline was laid down and triangulation carried out by R.E. Middleton. Once the Fife pier's position had been fixed, the rock was levelled and the site cleared. On the South Queensferry shore more work was necessary to accommodate the workshops, etc. Sixteen houses and sixty tenements were built for staff, many more having to travel by rail or ferry to the site. A telephone cable was laid across the Forth to ensure communication. Eventually an area

PLATE 35 Soundings for the site of the deep pier off Inch Garvie, 18 June 1884. Engineers: Sir John Fowler and Sir Benjamin Baker; contractor: Tancred Arrol; photographer: E. Carey

of more than 50 acres was occupied between 1886 and 1889 while fabrication of the girders took place. In addition, cement stores had to be erected.

In early 1883 the 1,200 ft-long Queensferry jetty was commenced. On its completion in the spring of 1884 the first caisson was launched. At Inch Garvie, the island in the estuary, the earliest work was the erection of wind gauges in the summer of 1882. A launching stage was built in April 1883, and then the site was levelled to 7 ft above high water, with 100 yd of sea wall to protect it.

With the completion of the main piers in March 1886 work could now begin on the superstructure, making extensive use of hydraulic machinery, and specially-developed plant. The central towers above the piers were erected using working platforms raised by hydraulic rams in sixteen lifts, with two to three days taken up with rivetting. Up to three lifts were achieved in a week. The Inch Garvie platform was raised into position between January and August 1887 by this process. As they were raised the platform girders were then stiffened and trussed using link chains from the recently demolished Hammersmith suspension bridges which had been bought by the contractors. The working platforms could only be raised to within 20 ft of the full height of the structure, by which stage they were very close together and looked unbalanced. Work had begun on the bottom members of the cantilevers when the platforms had reached the point of intersection of the diagonal struts and columns in the central towers.

PLATE 36 Relaxation on the bottom cantilever arm of the Forth Railway Bridge, showing working cage and rivetters' furnace. 13.75 in x 10.75 in. Engineers: Sir John Fowler and Sir Benjamin Baker; contractor: Tancred Arrol; photographer: E. Carey

With the completion of the cantilever in July 1889, preparation for the crucial last phase, the erection of the 346 ft 6 in central girder, could begin. Baker had been clear about how this should be done from the first: 'The closing lengths of key pieces at the centre of each 1,700 foot span will be put in on a windy day or at night, when there is little variation of temperature, and the details will be arranged that the key piece can be completed and the temporary inconvenience from changes of temperature.'[4] On 10 October the southern suspended span was finished, and on 6 November all was ready for completion. The bottom booms were connected but the temperature did not drop sufficiently for the final connection of the northern span of the top booms and key plates to be completed until 14 November. There then followed four months of hectic preparation to complete the bridge for railway traffic. On 21 January 1890 the first train crossed the bridge, some two months prior to the official opening on 4 March 1890.

The cantilever structure was originally estimated to require 42,000 tons of steel. In the event a further 6,000 were required, although 3–4,000 tons were returned as scrap. Of this *c.* 12,000 tons came from Siemens Works near Swansea, 38,000 tons from the Steel Company's two works near Glasgow, and 8,000 tons from Dalzell's Iron and Steel Works at Motherwell. In addition

PLATE 37 Forth Railway Bridge: constructing the central girder, September 1889. 14 in x 10.5 in. Engineers: Sir John Fowler and Sir Benjamin Baker; contractor: Tancred Arrol; photographer: P. Phillips/Photophane

over 4,000 tons of rivets were supplied by the Rivet Company of Glasgow.

The bridge not only represented a triumph of structural steel, it was also a tribute to the contractors who built it: a consortium of Joseph Phillips, Sir Thomas Tancred, (Sir) William Arrol and T.H. Falkiner, with the caisson work being sub-contracted to the specialist French engineer Coiseau. The bridge did, however, have its critics, particularly from an aesthetic viewpoint. They are best answered by the one man above all others responsible for the bridge – Benjamin Baker:

> It was impossible for anyone to pronounce authoritatively on the beauty of an object without knowing its functions. . . . It would be a ludicrous error to suppose that Sir John Fowler and he had neglected to consider the design from the artistic point of view. They did so from the very first. An arched form was admittedly graceful, and they had approximated their bridge to that form as closely as they could without suggesting false constructions and shams. They made the compression members strong tubes, and the tension members light lattice work, so that

> to any intelligent eye the nature of the stresses and the sufficiency of the members of the structure to resist them were emphasised at all points. It would have been futile to attempt to ornament the great cantilevers, and so, to keep the whole work in harmony, they studiously avoided any attempt at ornamentation of the piers, and people would search in vain even for a moulded capping, or cornice throughout the whole work. The object had been so to arrange the leading lines of the structure as to convey an idea of strength and stability. This, in such a structure, seemed to be at once the truest and highest art.[5]

Despite the dominance of railway transport in the Victorian period, important road bridges were erected at this time, particularly in an urban context. Indeed, one of Robert Stephenson's most famous railway bridges, the high-level bridge at Newcastle-upon-Tyne, was designed to take both road and rail traffic on separate decks. Such road bridges as were built tended to reflect railway bridge designs. They were built as urban growth, and increased traffic, made existing river crossings inadequate either structurally or in terms of capacity.

In London problems with the eighteenth-century crossings of the Thames became increasingly acute as the nineteenth century progressed. The majority of these outside the City were enshrined in Acts of Parliament, which presented peculiar problems in securing improvements, not finally resolved until they were taken over by the Metropolitan Board of Works in 1877. The bridge replacement programme had begun earlier when a new masonry London Bridge had been opened in 1832. This had a significant effect on the flow of the river upstream of the bridge as the replacement presented less of an obstacle to the tide, and no longer dammed the river behind.

Replacement of the two eighteenth-century masonry bridges at Blackfriars and Westminster followed. Westminster (see Plate 21) had been plagued with problems since its construction, James Walker remarking in 1846, '. . . it is like a patient whose constitution I did not make, which has been in the hands of the doctors from the day it was built to the present time.'[6] The new river regime was the last straw, dangerously exposing the foundations. After thirty years deliberations, the bridge was replaced between 1854 and 1862 to a design of Thomas Page. Shortly after (1860–9) Blackfriars Bridge was replaced because of worries about scour. Joseph Cubitt was the engineer. Both these bridges were the concern of public authorities, the City (Blackfriars) and Central Government (Westminster), and could thus call on reasonable financial resources, unlike the toll companies responsible for many of the other structures. The replacements reflected the changing use of structural materials. Masonry was ruled out by expense, not

to return until the Metropolitan Board of Works replacement programme took over at the end of the century. Westminster used both cast and wrought iron in its arch structure, reflecting the gradual phasing out of cast iron by this time. Blackfriars was a wrought-iron arch structure with cast iron reduced to a purely decorative role.

Of the bridges the Metropolitan Board of Works acquired, the eighteenth-century bridges at Battersea and Putney, and the early suspension bridge (1824–7) at Hammersmith were replaced by structures designed by Sir Joseph Bazalgette with help from his son Edward. Exceptionally for the period, granite arches were used at Putney. Other new crossings built at this time were Lambeth (1861–2), designed by Peter W. Barlow; Chelsea (1851–8), another Thomas Page design; and Albert Bridge (1871–3), designed by R.M. Ordish. To these should be added the short-lived Hungerford Suspension Bridge, designed by I.K. Brunel. Completed in 1845, it was replaced in 1860 by the present railway bridge. All these bridges shared a suspension form, although only Chelsea and Hungerford were strictly speaking suspension bridges. Both Albert and Lambeth were stiffened structures relying on distinctive arrangements of stays (Albert) and lattice work (Lambeth) rather than a more traditional arrangement. Ordish's design was successfully exported to Prague and Singapore. Because of the width of the Thames, and the needs of navigation, all these bridges had substantial spans, and were impressive feats of civil engineering.

Aside from the piers at Hungerford and Hammersmith the earliest surviving bridge of the period is the cast-iron arch railway bridge at Barnes, designed by Locke and Errington, and built 1846–9. By and large the railway bridges were built in the 1860s, and although much modified and strengthened, most have survived in a recognizable form to this day. Unlike the early road bridges they were designed for more realistic loads and without similar restraints of finance.

One of London's landmarks today is Tower Bridge, a most uncharacteristic bridge. By the end of the nineteenth century, pressure for a crossing of the river below London Bridge was irresistible. The Metropolitan Board of Works engineers were working on designs for a vehicle tunnel at Blackwall and wanted to build a bridge near the Tower of London. Sir Joseph Bazalgette put forward designs for a steel arch in 1870, but in the event the City, with its financial resources and political power, took over responsibility. Work began in 1886 on the bridge, which was designed by Sir John Wolfe Barry, with Horace Jones as architect. Its unusual form was dictated in part by the requirement to provide an opening span for navigation up to London Bridge, and to maintain pedestrian access via a high-level footbridge while the

PLATE 38 The building of the Hungerford Railway Bridge, Charing Cross. Pictures of London's bridges provide examples of almost all the various forms of photography of the time, from the early days of Fox Talbot's calotype of the original Hungerford Bridge (1845), through popular views such as stereocards of the London Stereoscopic Company, to some of the earliest civil engineering record photographs, such as this one, and others taken at Blackfriars and Westminster at much the same time. Engineer: J. Hawkshaw; contractors: Cochrane & Company (ironwork), Lucas (station)

bridge was open. The bridge combines a bascule-opening span with side spans suspended from trussed chains. This stiffening arrangement was similar to that used by Schnirch in Vienna a generation earlier, although a St Andrews truss-type arrangement was preferred to a simple Warren truss. The main towers housed hydraulic equipment for raising the bascules and power lifts for pedestrians. They are of particular interest as early examples of steel-framed structures.

Perhaps the most famous road bridge of the period was the Clifton Suspension Bridge, designed by I.K. Brunel. Brunel won a competition for a bridge to span the Avon Gorge near Bristol in 1831. His design for a 702 ft-span suspension bridge was considerably longer than Telford's bridge across the Menai Straits, which had a central span of 580 ft. If it had been executed at the time it would have been the longest suspension bridge in the world. Although work was begun the bridge company ran out of money and the bridge was never completed in his lifetime, although photographs survive to record its various stages of incompleteness. The towers were built, and the ironwork for the chains ordered in 1840. No real further progress was made, and the ironwork was sold in 1849 to be used subsequently in the Saltash Bridge. On Brunel's death colleagues at the Institution of Civil Engineers resolved to complete the bridge as a tribute to Brunel. The engineers were W.H. Barlow and John Hawkshaw. Hawkshaw was at the time (1859) involved in the demolition of Brunel's

PLATE 39 Clifton Suspension Bridge, construction suspended, *c.* 1854. Engineer: I.K. Brunel

Hungerford Suspension Bridge (see Plate 38) to make way for the Charing Cross Railway Bridge, and so they were able to reuse the chains. The bridge was finally completed in 1864.

NOTES

1. R. Stephenson, *Chester and Holyhead Railway, Report . . . upn the experiments made to ascertain the practicability of erecting a tubular bridge across the Merian Straits*, London, 1846, p. 6.
2. T. Mackay, *The Life of Sir John Fowler*, 1900, p. 8.
3. W. Westhofen, *The Forth Bridge*, 1890, p. 6.
4. B. Baker, *The Forth Bridge: paper read to the British Association*, 1882.
5. B. Baker, Lecture to Edinburgh Literary Institute, 27 November 1889. Quoted in T. Mackay, *The Life of Sir John Fowler*, 1900, pp. 314–15.
6. *Report of the Select Committee on the present state of Westminster Bridge*, 1846, paragraph 1305.

CHAPTER SIX

London's Railways and Termini

You must have railways in a place like London. In a few years we should not be able to exist here, the streets would be so blocked up with omnibuses.

Sir Benjamin Baker, Minute of Evidence no. 995, House of Commons Select Committee on London Central (Subway) Railway Bill, 1 July 1890.

London's importance in the development of the British railway network has tended to be overlooked. The achievements of George and Robert Stephenson in introducing steam locomotion in the north-east and latterly the Liverpool–Manchester Railway have dominated popular railway history at the expense of other events. The economic and political importance of London within Britain inevitably means it forms a major chapter of Victorian railway achievement. The acreage in London devoted to railway enterprise by the 1880s amounted to that of a fair sized town. Building railways in a crowded urban setting created engineering problems and innovative solutions, and the capital encouraged the railway companies to indulge in prestigious projects involving great engineering.

Despite the railway tradition in colliery areas, the world's first independent public railway was in London: the Surrey Iron Railway. It was opened in 1803, following an Act of Parliament in 1801, and was designed by William Jessop. London was also the location of one of the first exhibitions of steam locomotive power – by Trevithick in 1808. However, despite the use of railways in dock construction, there were no real developments as a result of either of these events until the 1820s when, with an eye on developments in the north, various schemes began to be floated for railway links between London and other provincial centres. It was not until the 1830s that any of these began to be realized. One reason for this delay must have been the distances involved and the capital thus required to float a company successfully. Opposition of landowners and the Parliamentary inexperience of engineers and promoters also played a part.

London's size and variety meant that a wide range of motives could induce people to promote a railway: commuter traffic, freight traffic, speed of travel, rivalry between provincial centres. This was reflected in the earliest lines to be built in the capital. The first main line out of London to obtain Parliamentary approval was the London–Birmingham line (1833). The first line to be opened, however, was the London–Greenwich line (Act 1833, opened 1836). While the former aimed to link the capital to a provincial manufacturing district, the latter offered to save time on a popular journey into London, and capture coach and river traffic. The London–Greenwich can be seen as the first commuter line, and the first to see a link between property speculation and railway development. The twentieth-century development of 'Metroland' had its origins in the idea of renting out the arches of the London–Greenwich line as housing. The London–Birmingham, and its successor, the London and North Western Railway, did little to encourage commuter traffic, nor did the Great Western and Great Northern. For the companies running services to the east and south-east, which lacked the freight and long-haul traffic, however, commuter traffic offered an alternative route to economic prosperity.

Estimates of freight traffic played an important part in promoting the early railways. The remains of vast marshalling yards, at King's Cross, Camden, Stratford, Nine Elms, Shoreditch and the Bricklayers Arms, many currently being redeveloped, serve as a reminder of the economic importance of this aspect of the railways' activities. Despite the intentions of the railway companies themselves, growth in freight traffic was slow. Coal was not brought into London by rail until 1845, but by 1856 railways were carrying over 25 per cent of the coal trade. King's Cross, with its links with the north-east, was the centre of this, and developed extensive coal drops, some linking with canal traffic, to supply the London market. When the links through London were built via Farringdon and Blackfriars the Great Northern Company even attempted to supply the rest of the south-east. The Midland Railway built its own drops and yards, supplying coal from the Midland coalfields, which was cheaper than that supplied by the Great Northern Railway from the North-eastern and South Yorkshire coalfields. Aside from the coal trade the King's Cross-St Pancras site specialized in potatoes (King's Cross) and Burton Beer (St Pancras), with the latter being stored in the vast sub-basement beneath St Pancras station. The combined King's

PLATE 40 St Pancras station under construction. 10 in x 8 in. Engineer: W.H. Barlow; contractor: Waring; ironwork: Butterley & Company; photography: Butterley site staff

Cross-St Pancras goods yards amounted to a 134 acre site in the centre of London, a major monument to the importance of railways to the economy of London in the second half of the nineteenth century.

The scale of the London railway enterprise of the Victorian era is a source of wonder in itself, but in a civil engineering sense it is the railway termini which invoke most wonder today. The development of London's termini was, like the railway system itself, patchy. The earliest terminus, that of the London–Greenwich at London Bridge, never really had a chance to be properly developed. Almost as soon as it was planned the Parliamentary requirement for other railway companies south of the river to have their terminus there meant it had to be modified, and for nearly thirty years it was modified, added to and developed to take more lines, and latterly through traffic to new termini in the City and West End.

Euston was architecturally altogether more ambitious. At great expense a Doric arch – the tallest structure in London apart from St Paul's – was erected at the entrance, and a Great Hall erected for passengers' and shareholders' facilities. These buildings were, however, swallowed up in subsequent development which con-

PLATE 41 Paddington station, Metropolitan District Railway. 9.5 in x 7.5 in. Engineer: J. Fowler; contractor: Waring, Kelk & Lucas; photographer: H. Flather (in the photograph with a camera?)

cealed their architectural excellence in a confused clutter of additional hotel and office accommodation. In an engineering sense the initial terminal buildings were very modest: simple iron-roofed sheds presenting no great innovation or engineering achievement. Modest stations were in fact the rule, the cost of land in London and the initial capital outlay on railway construction discouraging company directors from the lavish outlay expended by the London–Birmingham Company. In addition, as a result of an 1846 Commission on London's termini, railways were excluded from a central area approximately bounded by the modern Circle Line, and lavish termini in what would then have been open fields or poor suburbs would have had little justification.

A new phase of station construction began in the 1850s at Paddington and King's Cross. From the first, the Great Western Railway Company had intended a major terminus, and secured the Paddington site while further funds were being raised. The resultant station erected 1851–4 comprised three roof spans of 70 ft, 102 ft and 68 ft respectively, with two 50 ft transepts. Its design was the result of a collaboration between I.K. Brunel as Company Engineer, and Matthew Digby Wyatt.

> The principle adopted by them was to avoid any recurrence to existing styles and to make the experiment of designing everything in accordance with the structural purpose or nature of the materials employed, iron and cement . . .[1]

The division between architect and engineer, while similar to elsewhere, with Brunel responsible for the overall layout and engineering design, and Wyatt for the architectural details, seems to have been more on a basis of cooperation rather than division of labour. Elsewhere the engineer had overall control, but generally confined himself to the train sheds, platforms, etc., and the architect was responsible for the station buildings and hotel.

King's Cross, like Paddington, took over from a temporary terminus. Unlike all the other termini, the civil engineering content of its design dominated the architectural treatment. Unusually for the period, timber rather than iron was chosen as the main structural support for the roof. Two laminated timber trusses of 105 ft span were used. Regrettably they had to be replaced in iron (1868 (east side) and 1887 (west side)). As successive termini were built ever wider spans were sought, at Victoria (1860–2, 129 ft maximum), Charing Cross (1864, 164 ft), Cannon Street (1863–6, 190 ft 4 in), and finally St Pancras (1868, 240 ft). All of these made use of an arch form, either with a crescent-shaped truss, or tied arch. The termini at Victoria, Charing Cross, Cannon Street, and also at Blackfriars, were the result of the success of the

PLATE 42 King's Cross, Metropolitan line, under construction. Fowler used a photograph of the Metropolitan line under construction in support of his evidence in favour of the Central London (Subway) Railway Bill in July 1890. 10 in x 8 in. Engineer: Sir John Fowler; contractor: Smith & Knight

railway companies south of London in securing access to the centre, as the value of railway transport became more generally recognized. This process had begun at Waterloo where the London and South Western Railway built a new terminus in 1845–8. In the City, likewise, the Great Eastern Railway removed its main terminus across Bishopsgate from Shoreditch to Liverpool Street (1871–5), alongside the suburban North London Railway's Broad Street Station (1865).

The successful design and construction of the large-span railway roofs reflected the advances in civil engineering between the 1830s and '60s, and in particular the experience gained by the ironfounders in the dockyard structures of the 1830s and '40s. Contemporaries saw a continuity in concept between the Crystal Palace, in which Wyatt was heavily involved, and Paddington Station. Although some arguments were put forward that the wider-span roofs offered more flexibility in layout of platforms and transfer of rolling stock, the spectacle seems to have been the major motive. The railway companies and their engineers vied with each other to demonstrate which was the most impressive company.

St Pancras wins all the accolades. It symbolized the Midland Railways' newfound freedom from the restrictions of limited access to other companies' London termini, notably King's Cross. Its roof remained the widest span in the world for twenty-five years. It was designed by William Henry Barlow with assistance from R.M. Ordish. Unlike earlier wide spans its arch was not trussed by ties, but rather with trusses within the arch ribs themselves. Aside from the impressive design concept the station is a tribute to the skill of the Butterley Company, in actually fabricating and erecting the massive ribs. An enormous temporary staging, moved on rails, in three sections, supporting two ribs at a time and weighing 580 tons, was erected. It was able to erect the roof at a rate of one rib per week. The Butterley Company were sufficiently proud of the process to photograph it. The importance of the ironmasters in developing these large-span structures is difficult to ignore. The earliest wide-span structure – the (153 ft 6 in) Liverpool Lime Street roof (1849) – was designed by Richard Turner, who supplied the ironwork design for Kew Palm House. New Street Birmingham (1854, *c.* 211 ft span) was built by Fox Henderson who had done much work in the dockyards and at Crystal Palace.

With the spate of terminus developments in the 1860s, problems of interconnections for passengers through London traffic became acute. In addition the companies with termini more remote from the City wanted an improved infrastructure for their passengers. The result was the construction of the world's first underground urban railway, the Metropolitan line, which was opened between Paddington and Farringdon in 1863, and extended west to

PLATE 43 Construction of Metropolitan District Railway station, *c.* 1866–8. The contractor's truck was running on plateways, which permitted it to run off the track and onto the streets. An important feature of this and other photographs taken by Flather is the record they provide of the construction process, including navvies at work. 9.5 in x 7.5 in. Engineer: J. Fowler; contractor: Waring, Kelk & Lucas; photographer: H. Flather

Hammersmith in 1864. This line was largely built using cut and cover construction, by excavating along the line of the Euston/ Pentonville Road, and covering with brick arches or iron girder-supported structures. The line attracted much popular attention, as can be seen in the dignitaries who attended the opening, but travellers were badly inconvenienced by the steam traction. Despite this the line was extended eastwards to Moorgate (1865), Liverpool Street (1875), Aldgate (1876), and Whitechapel (1884), and south and west via Kensington (1864), as the Metropolitan District Railway, to complete the 'inner' circle in 1884.

The Metropolitan and Metropolitan District railways demonstrated the traffic advantage of underground transport in an urban setting, but they were very expensive and disruptive. The southern segment between Westminster and Blackfriars was made possible by the construction of the Victoria Embankment and low level main drainage sewer, which provided the space within the reclaimed land behind the Embankment for the line. These railways saw extensive use of Portland cement concrete, including

PLATE 44 Construction of the Metropolitan District Railway. 9.5 in x 7.5 in. Engineer: J. Fowler; contractor: Waring, Kelk & Lucas; photographer: H. Flather

an early concrete bridge, and presented acute engineering problems associated with excavation in confined locations in London clay. These problems, and the disruptive effects, were recorded by Henry Flather in his series of photographs for the contractor. Inevitably problems occurred including the dramatic failure of the Fleet sewer near Farringdon. The result of the experience of excavating in London clay was summarized by Benjamin Baker in 1881. This was a seminal paper in the development of the science of soil mechanics, based as it was on a series of detailed case studies, many of which related to the railways.

The problems of railway construction in London clay had been experienced in the 1830s and '40s with the first railway cuttings on the London–Birmingham and London–Croydon railways. The bulking or swelling capacity and the earth pressure exerted became notorious, and it was only later that its potential as a tunnelling medium was realized. The experience of Marc Brunel's Thames Tunnel had deterred further experiments with tunnels beneath the Thames. Despite the ultimate engineering success of

PLATE 45 Group including W.E. Gladstone at the opening of the Metropolitan Railway, 24 May 1862. 15.5 in x 9.75 in. Engineer: J. Fowler; contractor: Kelk, Waring Brothers and Lucas

the tunnel, and the fact it demonstrated underwater tunnels could be built by miners using a protective shield, the costs in financial and human terms were horrific. The Tunnel Company was not a financial success even after the tunnel was opened in 1843, and its conversion to the world's first underwater railway, the East London line between Whitechapel and New Cross in 1869, provided it with a *raison d'être* which was otherwise lacking. The cost of the cut and cover method, and success of the Metropolitan and District railways encouraged a fresh look at tunnelling methods.

While constructing Lambeth Bridge in 1862 Peter Barlow made use of cast-iron cylinders for the bridge's pier foundations. He saw the potential of such cylinders for horizontal tube construction, and in 1864 took out a patent for applying this method to tunnelling. It was developed further when the Tower Subway was built 1869–70 between Tower Hill and Southwark, by Greathead, a pupil of Barlow. This was initially designed for a cable railway, but the prohibitive fares deterred passengers. It was not until the 1880s that a successful railway was launched – the City and South London. Work began in October 1886, and it was completed between the City and Stockwell in 1890. Although originally planned as a cable railway, it was opened as an electric railway reflecting the great advances in electric railway traction in the decade since 1879 when Siemens had demonstrated its practicability. The City and South London Railway, as the world's first tube railway was known, was made possible by the engineering experience built up by Barlow and Greathead, and Benjamin Baker. Baker's evidence on the scheme's practicability was crucial in obtaining Parliamentary assent. Thus within fifty years the work of civil engineers had brought London's railway network from a few haphazard beginnings to a vast infrastructure which remains the basis for much of the capital's passenger transport today.

NOTES

1. Illustrated London News, 8 July 1854.

CHAPTER SEVEN

Harbours and Docks

Harbours and docks are essential for the safe and expeditious carrying on of the commerce of the world

Vernon Harcourt, 1885.

Maritime power was at the heart of the British Empire. Since British supremacy had been established over the Dutch in the late seventeenth century, Great Britain had been the world's premier trading nation. With an expanding industrial base, a rapidly increasing population, and a growing overseas empire, a demand for improvements in port infrastructure to facilitate imports and exports was inevitable in the nineteenth century. The increased size of vessels, and other improvements in propulsion achieved by civil engineers, required consequent improvements in dock and harbour entrances, berthing facilities, channel depth, etc. Rivalry between ports ensured there was plenty of work for civil engineers all over the country.

Of all the forces of power in nature civil engineers might choose to direct in the pursuit of their profession, that of the sea presented the greatest challenge. Dock and harbour engineering involved designing structures to withstand the regular pounding of waves, the effects of silt and scour, wind and tide. Their scale had to be massive to withstand such forces over a period of time.

One important feature of the period was the scientific study devoted to a better understanding of the forces involved. This had been a notable feature of Smeaton's work at the Eddystone Lighthouse in the eighteenth century, where he had developed an interlocking form of masonry construction to withstand the wave forces, and carried out important research into the properties of cement to be sure it could survive underwater exposure. Smeaton's mantle, at least as far as lighthouses were concerned was taken up by the Stevenson family, who were responsible for the design of most of the lighthouses around the Scottish coast. They developed instruments to measure the force of waves.

PLATE 46 Eddystone Lighthouse. Engineer: John Smeaton

According to Thomas Stevenson the average force at the Skerryvore Lighthouse in water was 2,086 lb per sq ft, and the maximum he recorded 6,083 lb. No matter how much care was taken in design the forces of nature were difficult to resist in these circumstances. At Wick in 1872 a mass of masonry 45 ft x 21 ft, weighing 1,350 tons was dislodged. As well as wave force, wave height, and wave direction and generation were important in safe design of harbour facilities. Important work was carried out by John Scott Russell under the auspices of the British Association in the 1830s and '40s. Russell estimated wave height in British waters at 27 ft, which compared favourably with the 50–60 ft waves regularly seen around the Cape of Good Hope. This meant that protective harbour works were essential if ships were to be berthed safely in British waters and led to a series of Parliamentary inquiries into British harbours in the nineteenth century, and the construction of designated harbours of refuge. This continued a tradition of public involvement in harbour works which had been seen in the work of Telford and Rennie around the coasts of Scotland and Ireland earlier in the century with the aim of reviving the Scottish Highland economy in particular. Many of the smaller harbours thus constructed were overtaken by the revolution in ship construction which rendered the majority of the harbours obsolete for all save coastal traffic and small fishing vessels.

The more important ports were largely financed by private capital, such as that from London, or local boards or trusts created by acts of Parliament, which could borrow money to finance works, and then pay for them out of harbour dues. With the coming of the railways some of the smaller harbour trusts were bought out by the railway companies which played an increasing role in developing their trade. In addition there were important works carried out

PLATE 47 Hermitage Breakwater in progress, St Helier, Jersey, 1877. Engineer: Sir John Coode; photographer: Coode's resident engineer

with the needs of the Royal Navy in mind. The great breakwater at Plymouth, begun by John Rennie and completed by his son Sir John, was 5,100 ft long. The scale of the work and its location, combined with the imperfect understanding of the forces at work meant that the design had to be modified as work progressed. Covered originally as a rubble mound, with a slope of 3:1 on the seaward side, storm damage in 1824 led to a radical rethink. The sea slope was altered to 5:1, it was paved with granite set in cement, and concreted from low water level to the top of the breakwater. By 1847 more than £1.5 million had been spent on it.

Breakwaters generally presented the greatest challenge to the civil engineer, and still pose problems today as evinced by the damage recently caused at Sines in Portugal. In its simplest form a breakwater was just a mound of rubble, designed to produce an area of calm water on its land side. For a breakwater to operate successfully it has to be aligned correctly for prevailing winds and waves. Rubble mound structures inevitably involved regular maintenance. To attempt to reduce this, large blocks of masonry could be placed on the sea slope to act as protection. A superstructure could also be added to protect against the action of waves overtopping the breakwater. This presented problems of settlement as, unless the rubble was placed carefully, it was unlikely to withstand the superimposed load of a masonry wall, which was also liable to be undermined by the action of the sea on the rubble. In water of more modest depth where the bottom was hard, an upright sea wall could be constructed as at Scarborough. The foundations could be built up at low water from the base rock. Where this was not possible concrete bags were placed until a firm foundation could be created. Divers could also be used, as they were at Dover, to place masonry.

Breakwaters were expensive and construction took a long time, the work at Dover taking over twenty years. Problems were only discovered as construction proceeded as at Plymouth. At Tynemouth, where a breakwater was intended to create a harbour of refuge at the mouth of the Tyne for coastal shipping as well as improve navigation on the Tyne, work began in 1856. By 1863 it was clear the rubble mound was unstable at low water level. Foundations were lowered 12 ft below low water, but in 1867 a violent storm undermined both breakwaters, necessitating underpinning the foundations, replacing the rubble heart of the breakwater with concrete, and placing concrete blocks. In some cases the cost became too great, and works were abandoned, as at St Helier and St Catherine's in Jersey.

Blockwork was a feature of quay walls as well as breakwaters, and specialist plant was developed by engineers like William Parkes and Sir John Coode, and supplied by specialist firms like Stothert and Pitt. With cranes known as 'Hercules', 'Titan' and

'Goliath', this heavy civil engineering plant became a regular feature of harbour works involving extensive blockwork.

Quay walls were massive retaining walls, and had to be designed to resist not just earth pressure but also the hydrostatic pressure of the water in often saturated ground. To some extent this could be equalized in docks by the pressure of the water they enclosed, but dry docks had to be emptied regularly to permit work to be carried out on the ships entering. Although early dry docks of timber were constructed, they became increasingly all-masonry structures, performing as inverted arches. Watertightness was always a problem and pumping was an important feature of their design.

To support the weight of quay walls, good foundations were necessary. Although satisfactory profiles for the walls had been developed by engineers like Jessop and Rennie around 1800, stability remained a problem. At Liverpool the base rock generally provided a satisfactory foundation, but even here piling was needed; as the dock network was extended from the central area it became increasingly necessary as the rock foundation shelved ever deeper. An alternative to piling was cylinder foundations, as seen at Surrey Docks, and on the Thames embankment. Early quay walls were stone or brick, but concrete was increasingly used, with masonry only on the face, and eventually superseded it entirely as concrete proved its durability in seawater. Such large masonry structures were expensive, and open timber jetties offered a cheaper alternative. They were used at Victoria Docks on the southern side where there were originally open jetties and no quay walls.

Behind the quays were the warehouses and transit sheds. The enclosed dock systems with their massive quayside warehouses, so typical of the early London docks, were gradually superseded by more open facilities and transit sheds. The architecturally-impressive warehouses at Albert Dock in Liverpool were arguably out-of-date before they were built, overtaken by the increased size of shipping, and the need for quayside railway access rather than direct ship–warehouse storage. Large warehouses continued to be built, however, and where they survive provide an atmospheric reminder of the age of sail and Victorian maritime prosperity. Their blend of brick, iron and stonework gives them an austere functional aesthetic whose conversion to other uses can only ever be partially successful.

London was the greatest port in the world at the time, handling over 11 million tons of cargo a year in the 1880s. Congestion in the Pool of London arising from the eighteenth-century growth in trade – an increase in foreign tonnage handled from 158,000 to 620,000 between 1705 and 1794 – and concern over pilferage, led to a spate of dock construction in the early years of the nineteenth century. Of these the West India Dock system in the Isle of Dogs was the largest civil engineering scheme hitherto attempted. These early dock schemes were the work of city businessmen and merchants specializing in the East and West India trade. A new type of entrepreneur emerged in the railway age, who had made their money and reputation out of railways. The first major addition to the heritage of Rennie, Jessop, Telford and the Walkers was the Victoria Dock scheme. This was a speculative venture financed by three of the great railway contractors – Samuel Morton Peto, Edward Ladd Betts, and Thomas Brassey, with the help of George Parker Bidder. They bought very cheaply a low-lying area of land, Plaistow Marshes in east London, and obtained Parliamentary sanction to build a dock. This was the first to be purpose-built to accommodate steamships, with an 80 ft entrance. It had the latest hydraulic machinery supplied by Sir William Armstrong, and was designed with rail communications in mind. The developers also acquired further land for future dock expansion should it be required. The Victoria Dock was opened in 1855, and rapidly became, in terms of tonnage, the busiest dock system in the port. In this the docks were undoubtedly helped by the conservative management of the competition: East and West India Docks did not get proper rail connections until the 1870s.

The success of the Victoria Dock encouraged others. In 1859 Nathaniel John Fenner, a Millwall merchant approached Robert Fairlie, a civil engineer, with a view to developing the land in the

PLATE 48 Lock gates, Millwall Docks, 1867. Engineer: Sir John Fowler; contractor: Kelk & Aird

south of the Isle of Dogs as a dock site. The Millwall Freehold Land and Canal Company was formed, with a particular view to increasing quayside accommodation for industrial sites in an area which at that time was booming as a centre of shipbuilding and associated trades. Little happened until Fenner and Fairlie approached William Wilson, a consultant civil engineer with a large number of contacts. Having deposited Parliamentary plans he got two major contractors, Kelk and Aird, interested in the scheme. Fenner and Fairlie were sidelined as contractors; Kelk and Aird saw an opportunity to make money. Sir John Fowler, by then one of the country's leading civil engineers, whose early professional experience had been in hydraulic works, was brought in as consultant, and Parliamentary approval became a formality. Finance was more of a problem, particularly with the crash of 1866, precipitated by the failure of the bankers Overend Gurney and Company, which had been heavily involved in engineering finance. The contractors Peto and Betts failed, and several of the Thames-side engineering firms. Although Aird's profited by Peto and Betts' failure, the scheme now lacked its original *raison d'etre*. From their opening in 1868 the Millwall Docks had to struggle to survive, relying on the ingenuity of their engineer Duckham, and shrewd financial management. The docks themselves were a relatively simple construction job. Their low-lying situation made excavation to the desired level relatively simple. Dock walls 28–30 ft high were built with a brick facing 2 ft thick tied into a concrete retaining wall 11 ft 6 in deep by bands of brickwork.

Even before the crash of 1866 the dock system had been in trouble. The early dock acts had provided a free water clause whereby ships using the docks could discharge into lighters servicing river wharves and warehouses, and thus evade the dock companies' quay and warehousing dues. This restricted their profitability, and meant a good deal of traffic was handled by wharves and warehouses independent of the dock companies, indeed the river wharfingers handled the bulk of coastal traffic throughout the century. In 1838 the East and West India Dock companies merged in an attempt to eliminate costly rivalry. The impact of the Victoria Dock led to a merger between the London, St Katharine's and Victoria Dock Companies, as the London and St Katharine's Dock Company in 1864. In the same year, south of the river, the Commercial and Grand Surrey Companies merged as the Surrey Commercial Dock Company. A period of ruinous competition ensued when between 1874 and 1880 the London and St Katharine's Dock Company built the Royal Albert Dock as an extension to the Victoria Dock. The dock was designed by Sir Alexander Rendel, and built by Lucas and Aird, to be capable of taking the larger vessels afloat and adding electric lighting to the facilities offered. The East and West India Company responded with Tilbury Docks, built 1882–6. The original contractors, Kirk and Randall, were sacked, the scheme being wildly over budget – £2.8 million compared with estimates of £1.1 million. Trade could only be tempted at a loss. In 1889 the management of the two major north river groupings was merged as one. Despite the undoubted engineering achievements of their construction, it was clear the trade of the port was being badly managed.

South of the river, by skilful promotion of existing strengths, the Surrey Docks maintained trade and custom. Concentrating on timber and grain, facilities were improved, with Canada Dock opened largely for grain in 1876.

London's main rival was Liverpool. The dock system was much older, and with the lack of suitable riverside accommodation much more extensive until the completion of Tilbury. Aside from the Lancashire hinterland, and in particular the cotton trade, Liverpool's main cargo was people. Special railway connections ran trains full of *émigrés* bound for North America down to the docks and Princes landing stage where they boarded all manner of vessels to transport them across the Atlantic. The engineer mainly responsible for facilitating this port development was Jesse Hartley who was appointed surveyor to the docks in 1824. He had drawn up a plan for the development of the port which was largely completed by 1857 when responsibility for the port, and the facilities at Birkenhead was transferred from the City Corporation to Mersey Docks and Harbour Board.

PLATE 49 Surrey Commercial Docks No. 7 Warehouse, 1885. 11.5 in x 9.5 in. Photographer: George H. Owen

Liverpool's extensive port facilities did not satisfy all its hinterland. Manchester merchants in particular were concerned about the level of port charges, and also rates on the Liverpool–Manchester Railway and the alternative Bridgewater Canal/ Mersey–Irwell Navigation. Despite the impact of the railway the Bridgewater Canal continued to carry barge traffic from the Mersey up to Manchester. From the 1820s ideas of a ship canal to Manchester had been floated, but it was not until the 1880s when the great Suez and Panama Canal project had excited world opinion, that serious interest was expressed. The engineer was Edward Leader Williams, previously engineer to the Bridgewater Navigation Company, and the original contractor was Thomas Walker. Work began on 11 November 1887 and within a year eleven thousand men were at work. Walker was an experienced contractor and capable of executing such a massive scheme. Unfortunately he died in 1889, and the work had to be completed in part by direct labour, and partly by Jackson & Wills. The Ship Canal was one of the largest British construction projects of the century; 53,500,000 cubic yd of spoil were excavated by a team of up to 16,000 labourers, and a vast fleet of mechanical plant – 58 steam navvies, 97 steam excavators, 5 land dredgers, 194 steam cranes, 59 piling engines, 212 steam pumps, 182 stationary steam engines, with 173 locomotives and 6,300 wagons – available to remove the excavated earth. A flood of the excavation which took place in 1890 was turned to good effect by Leader Williams who used floating dredgers to continue the excavation. The result was to create an inland port for Manchester and Salford, capable of taking ocean-going vessels.

PLATE 50 Warrington–Walton new viaduct under construction, Manchester Ship Canal. Gelatino-bromide print, 8.5 in x 7.25 in. Engineer: Sir Edward Leader Williams; contractor: T.A. Walker; photographers: G.H. & H.C. Bayley

Elsewhere dock and harbour improvements were generally on a more modest scale, reflecting local needs and interests. Much trade was coastal, supplying London in particular with essentials. In the north-east, the coal trade provided the dominant reason for improvements. The River Tyne was the main route for coal traffic. Waggonways and latterly railways brought coal down to the riverside staiths where it was emptied into keels (barges) and transported down river to colliers. Despite proposals for navigation improvements from the eighteenth century onwards by John Rennie and others, little was achieved by the middle of the nineteenth century.

Staiths had been improved by the introduction of coal drops enabling wagons to be lowered onto the ships' decks. The Corporation of Newcastle showed a remarkable reluctance to do anything save collect the dues from river traffic. In the second half of the century there was, however, a gradual improvement.

By 1885 a navigation depth of 22 ft had been achieved up to Newcastle. Progress with docks was similarly slow. The first was Northumberland Dock (built 1853–7), designed for the coal trade by John Plews, who had designed similar facilities in Cardiff. The river commissioners failed to provide additional facilities despite obtaining Parliamentary powers on three occasions (1857, 1861, 1865), until 1874 when Coble Dene was begun. It was not completed until 1884. In the meantime the North Eastern Railway Company's engineer, Thomas Elliott Harrison, had designed Tyne Dock, at Jarrow, built by Jackson Bean and Gow, 1855–7.

The ports of the North-east Coalfield had a traditional relationship with the railways dating from the first introduction of railways to bringing coal to the sea for export. Elsewhere ports benefited from the coming of the railways for other reasons. Ports along the south and south-east coasts had long-established trade links with the Continent. In addition to traditional trade in wine and spirits, they ferried passengers across the Channel, and some were designated packet stations from which mail was carried across the sea. Natural changes wrought by silt had already undermined the medieval pre-eminence of the Cinque Ports which had held a monopoly on continental trade. For ports in this area the coming of the railways would vitally affect the ports' prosperity.

PLATE 51 Southampton Dry Dock under construction, *c.* 1876. Engineer: Alfred Giles

PLATE 52 Richard Tangye with the hydraulic press used to launch the *Great Eastern*. 'We launched the *Great Eastern* and she launched us' [Tangye Brothers]'. 14 in x 11 in. Photographer: R. Howlett, 1857

Southampton, probably more than any other port, benefited from its railway connections. Despite its medieval importance, due in part to its proximity to Winchester, and as a centre of the medieval wool trade, the port had failed to grow, and was totally eclipsed by London and Liverpool. It had, however, several natural advantages with a sheltered position behind the Isle of Wight, a double tide, and natural scour provided by the action of the rivers Test and Itchen. More or less contemporaneously with the coming of the railways in 1836 the Southampton Dock Company was established, with Francis Giles as engineer, who was then the first engineer to the London and Southampton (London and South Western) Railway. The railway was completed in 1840, and in part recognition of this link Southampton replaced Falmouth as the chief packet station for transatlantic mail when the outer dock was opened. The design of the dock facilities was modified to enable the newly introduced Royal Mail steamers to be accommodated. The rail link allowed passengers to travel direct from dock side to London. The first (outer) dock had a 39 ft high quay wall. Ground conditions were very poor for sustaining the weight of dock walls, comprising a sandy clay which degenerated in parts to quicksand. The walls were founded on a timber platform, piled at the front face. Despite the care taken, the water pressure behind the wall caused continual movement which could only be alleviated by excavating the fill and thus relieving the pressure. A timber deck had to be used for quayside facilities rather than the more usual paved area on made-up ground. There were two dry docks attached. To cope with the increased traffic an inner dock was opened in 1851, and a third dry dock in 1854. To these were added increased facilities in the 1870s – a River Quay (1876), and a fourth dry dock (1876). By this time trade had reached 2 million tons a year. The railway company's involvement increased until in 1886 it financed the construction of the Empress Dock. At the time of its opening in 1890 it was the only British dock to have an entrance capable of taking the largest vessels afloat at any stage of the tide, paving the way for the twentieth-century growth of the port.

CHAPTER EIGHT

Public Health Engineering

The sewerage of nearly three million people had been brought to seethe and ferment under a burning sun, in a vast open cloaca lying in their midst.

London, 1858.[1]

The most durable, and least discussed, contribution of Victorian civil engineers to modern society was in the field of public health. Prior to the mid-nineteenth century two aspects of modern life taken for granted – constant water supply and efficient sewage disposal – were virtually unknown. The explosive growth of the urban population in the late eighteenth and early nineteenth centuries exposed the inadequacies of these existing urban water supplies and primitive sewerage systems. The seventeenth-century New River scheme had demonstrated that it was possible to provide wholesome water from a remote source to a large urban area, but other London companies continued to use the increasingly polluted Thames as a cheap source. It took the carnage of the cholera outbreaks of 1831–2 and the late 1840s to change the climate of public opinion sufficiently to produce legislative change. In the 1840s the work of Sir Edwin Chadwick and others in the sanitary reform movement demonstrated the clear link between impure water, inadequate or non-existent sewerage systems, and disease. To help solve these problems the sanitary reform movement needed to call on the expertise of the civil engineer, as Chadwick freely acknowledged in *The Sanitary Conditions of the Labouring Classes* (1842):

> That for the protection of the labouring classes and of the ratepayers against inefficiency and waste in all new structural arrangements for the protection of the public health, and to ensure that the expenditure will be beneficial, securities should be taken that all new local public works are devised and conducted by responsible officers qualified by the possession of the science and skill of civil engineers.[2]

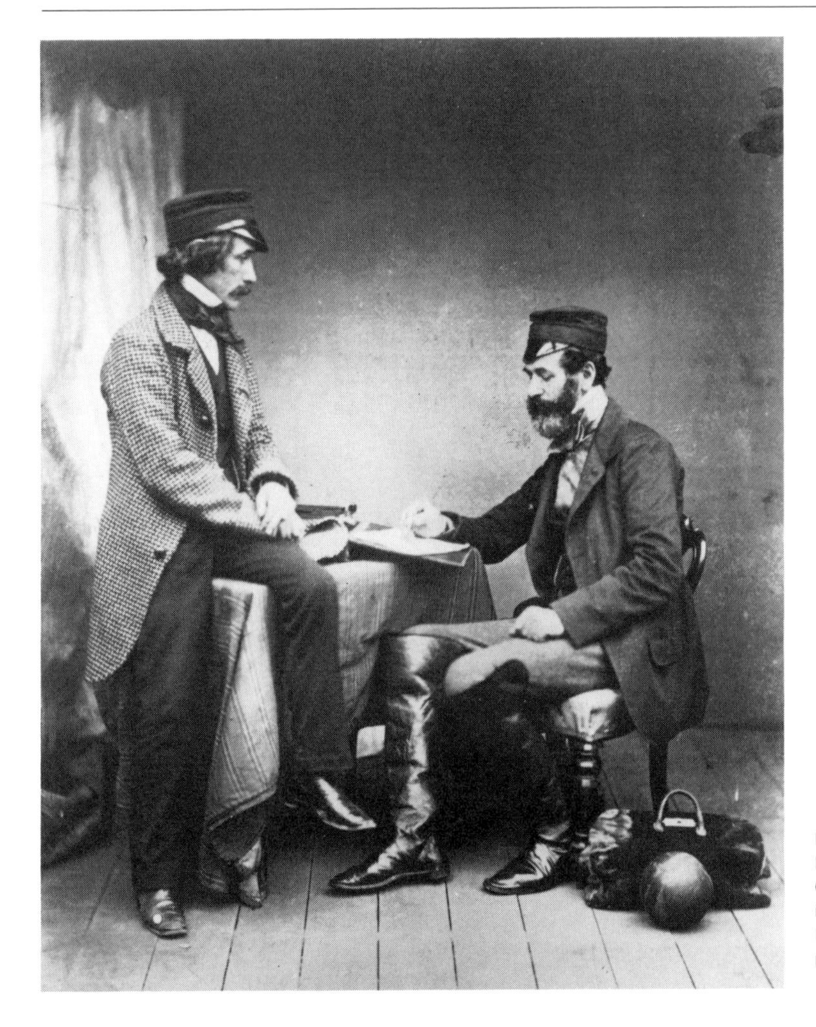

PLATE 53 Robert Rawlinson and Dr Sutherland, the Sanitary Commission for the Crimea. 7.75 in x 3.75 in, salt print. Photographer: R. Fenton; publisher: T. Agnew, 25 March 1856

When the Government appointed a Sanitary Commission in response to public outcry over the sanitary conditions of the troops serving in Crimea it thus seemed logical a civil engineer, Robert Rawlinson, should be appointed.

Although some of the famous names in civil engineering, such as Thomas Telford and Robert Stephenson, were called on occasion to advise on public health engineering, the public health revolution was largely the achievement of specialists like Rawlinson, and other forgotten names – Bazalgette, Bateman, Hawksley, Taylor, Simpson and Binnie. The water-supply engineers built on the achievements of canal engineers in developing watertight earth dam structures in the late eighteenth and early nineteenth centuries. To this was added improved theoretical understanding of hydraulics, the application of steam power to pump water and sewage, and innovations such as James Simpson's slow sand filters developed at Chelsea Waterworks in the 1820s, and the Metropolitan Board of Works sponsorship of improved concrete quality in their main drainage works.

The most obvious achievement was that of Sir Joseph Bazalgette and his colleagues responsible for the design and construction of the sewerage system for the capital in the 1850s and '60s. Bazalgette came to public health engineering having nearly killed himself in the frenetic atmosphere of railway work in the railway mania of the 1840s. His early training had been in land-drainage works in Ireland, and his subsequent career demonstrated his mastery of all branches of engineering. The public health of the capital in the 1840s had led to the establishment of a Metropolitan Commission of Sewers in 1848, and Bazalgette joined its technical staff in 1849.

The main task of the commission's engineers was to deal with the sewage of the capital, which at that time, Bazalgette subsequently remarked:

> . . . passed down sewers from the high ground at right angles to the Thames into the low grounds adjoining the Thames, where at high water it was pent up in the sewers, forming great elongated cesspools of stagnant sewage, and then when the tide

PLATE 54 Concrete batching plant, Northern Outfall Works, *c.* 1860. 7.5 in x 6 in. Engineer: Sir Joseph Bazalgette; contractor: Furness; photographer: W. Brown (?)

PLATE 55 Victoria embankment and the Metropolitan District railway with dignitaries visiting near Hungerford Bridge, *c.* 1866. 11.5 in x 7.5 in. Engineers: Sir Joseph Bazalgette and John Fowler; contractors: Waring, Kelk & Lucas (railway); Furness Aird (embankment)

went down and opened the outlets that sewage was poured into the river at low water at a time when there was very little water in the river.[3]

Under the initial leadership of Frank Foster, and with the advice of consultants like Robert Stephenson, the commission's engineers drew up a broad design for the main drainage of London using intercepting sewers north and south of the river to take the sewage down river beyond the built-up area. Nothing practical was achieved, however, until the commission was replaced in 1856 by the Metropolitan Board of Works, with a much wider remit and more extensive powers. Bazalgette was engineer to the board almost throughout its life. For the first ten years or so he was almost exclusively concerned with the main drainage of London. The intercepting sewers were brick-built with a fall of 2 ft per mile from west to east. At pumping stations in eastern London the sewage was raised into outfall sewers which terminated at outfall works at Crossness and Beckton. In all 80 miles of sewers were involved, seven pumping stations, and major quantities of brickwork, concrete and ironwork. Detailed specifications were drawn up, and important research was carried out to develop concrete quality. The printed contract documents and lithographed contract drawings were part of a meticulous attention to detail in the contract procedure which are the basis of civil engineering contracts today. The most visible feature of the drainage works today are the Thames embankments, which on the north side incorporated the low-level sewer and the Metropolitan District Railway. The Victoria Embankment was built within cast-iron cofferdams to a depth of at least 20 ft below Ordnance Datum (OD). It was founded on 12 ft 6 in of concrete, with a brick wall on top. The river wall was faced with granite to a depth of 8 ft below OD. The wall, subway and sewer were tied in by cross walls every 6 ft of 18 in thickness. They reclaimed about 52 acres of land in central London, and transformed an unsanitary mixture of wharves and mud into some of the most elegant streetscapes in London.

The scale of the engineering works undertaken by the Metropolitan Board of Works overshadows the more modest engineering involved in the contemporary construction of the Loch Katrine scheme for Glasgow's water scheme. Its designer, John Frederick de la Trobe Bateman, was *the* water engineer of the century. He designed forty-three large dams, and at the peak of his practice around 1870 was involved in over twenty schemes a year, but the Glasgow scheme was probably his finest.

Glasgow's first water supply company was set up in 1806 and a second followed in 1812. The former took over the latter in 1838. Their supplies were inadequate for the growing city and in 1852 Glasgow Corporation called on Bateman to advise on a scheme for constant water supply to the city. Bateman recognized that Loch

PLATE 56 Aqueduct through Loch Ard Forest, *c.* 1859. Loch Katrine water scheme, 1856–9. Engineer: John Frederick de la Trobe Bateman; contractor: R. Thomson & Sons; source: Strathclyde Regional Council

Katrine, some 36 miles away, could with minor modifications supply all the city's requirements for the foreseeable future. By raising the loch's natural level 4 ft with a modest dam, and having the outlet 3 ft below the existing natural outlet, the city would draw on the top 7 ft of surface water, supplying 50 million gallons a day. Apart from a modest further raising of the water level the Loch Katrine scheme has met all Glasgow's needs for the past century, and will do so for the foreseeable future. The main engineering features of the scheme were the aqueducts bringing the water from Loch Katrine through 13 miles of tunnels, open channels, and pipelines to Murdock, 10 miles from the city centre, where service reservoirs were built, from which the water could be distributed in two 36 in diameter cast-iron pipelines to the city. Work began in the spring of 1856, and the scheme was opened by Queen Victoria in 1859. It has all the hallmarks of true engineering genius. Using his engineering judgement Bateman was able to identify a seemingly remote water source which at modest cost could supply one of the major cities of the British Empire. No lavish engineering works were required, no need to demonstrate his mastery of large dam design. Fortunate are we today that the engineers saw fit to photograph their achievement, possibly the earliest surviving example of a large-scale photographic record of a civil engineering job in the United Kingdom after the reconstruction of Crystal Palace.

The heart of Bateman's professional practice was centred around the industrial towns of Lancashire and Yorkshire, and especially Manchester Waterworks. These works were characterized by large earth dams in the Pennine valleys. A professional photographer, James Mudd, more famous for his record photographs of locomotives for Beyer–Peacock, was employed to record some, at least, of these works. The Manchester scheme involved the construction of a series of seven earth dams in the Longdendale Valley, five for water supply, and two to provide 'compensation' water to mill owners down the Etherow Valley. The work began in 1848 and was not completed until 1877, although the scheme was supplying Manchester with water from 1850. Geological problems encountered included major landslips and appalling rock strata which made it difficult to find satisfactory foundations.

The safe construction of earth dams relied upon making them watertight by the use of an impermeable core. A trench was normally taken down below ground level to an impermeable rock layer, and carried up through the earth embankment. The trench was filled with wet (puddle) clay layers 6 in deep which were worked by men treading in the clay until it had reached the correct consistency, having been soaked and left overnight. If the embankment were not watertight there was a danger of it being washed out by the action of water penetrating through. In the case of the Woodhead Embankment the base rock was so badly fissured at the original site that in 1862 Bateman resolved to build a new embankment slightly downstream of the original, taking the cut-off wall down to a depth of 160 ft below the top of the original embankment, in a successful attempt to seal the dam. Bateman realized clay puddle was unable to withstand such a load of water, and concrete was used to fill the rock trench, rather than clay. This was the first complete concrete cut off. At the time of their construction these dams formed the largest series of reservoirs in the world.

Dams were only part of the story, and some towns, such as Birmingham, continued to rely on local streams and groundwater to supply their population for much of the century. All relied on steam power for the distribution of the water, and photographs of these steam engines reveal the pumping stations as the cathedrals of public health engineering.

After Bateman the most extensive Victorian water engineering practice was probably that of Thomas Hawksley. Hawksley established his reputation with his work for Trent (Nottingham) Waterworks in the 1830s. Here his advocacy of a constant water supply under pressure to customers' taps brought him to the attention of Chadwick and thus to the fore of the sanitation reform movement. His ability as a parliamentary witness brought him a steady stream of work of which one example was a continuing involvement at Liverpool. Here two companies competed to provide an inadequate supply of water. In 1847 the Corporation bought them out. Hawksley recommended they build a series of five earth dams to provide a series of reservoirs in the Rivington scheme. The spring water thus gathered was filtered through slow sand filters, and

PLATE 57 Woodhead second embankment under construction, *c.* 1874. Engineer: John Bateman; contractor: R. Thomson & Sons; photographer: J. Mudd

PLATE 58 Whitacre pumping station, Birmingham Waterworks, *c.* 1883. Engineer: John W. Gray; supplier: Boulton & Watt; photographer: H.J. Whitlock

PLATE 59 Vyrnwy Dam under construction, *c.* 1887. From a 4.25 in x 3.25 in gelatine dry-plate glass negative. Engineers: T. Hawksley, G. Deacon

transported through a 44 in diameter cast-iron pipeline the 17.3 miles to the city. The aqueduct was at the time of its opening (1857) the longest in the world.

Subsequently the population and demand for water grew so rapidly that by the 1870s the scheme was clearly inadequate. The Borough Engineer, George Deacon, appointed in 1871 at only twenty-eight years of age, was asked to investigate alternative sources of supply. Deacon had already demonstrated his ability when he developed a water waste meter, which helped alleviate the immediate supply crisis when it was introduced in 1873. In 1877 Hugh Williams, a civil engineer from Wigan, suggested Vyrnwy as a possible source, and Deacon adopted his suggestion. At first the corporation favoured a joint venture with Manchester at Ullswater, but while negotiations faltered Deacon persevered with detailed site investigations. Hawksley and Bateman were consulted and endorsed Deacon's scheme, and in 1879 the council adopted it. To assist in promoting the Bill through Parliament Hawksley was retained with Deacon as joint engineer. Deacon had identified an old rock barrier in the Vyrnwy valley as a suitable site to found the dam, and both he and Hawksley decided on a masonry dam rather than the more usual earth dam. As such it was the first large masonry dam to be designed in the United Kingdom.

The Vyrnwy Dam as built was one of the first to be designed using what would now be considered a reasonable understanding of the theoretical principles involved. Rankine, referring to a proposed masonry dam at Tansa near Bombay, had commented on French 'rational' design methods exhibited at Furens, which he felt had taken insufficient regard to determine lateral stresses. The same comments, with the recommendation that the line of resistance should be contained within the middle third of the dam, were published in *Engineering* in 1872 and must have been known to the designers. Hawksley was appointed engineer-in-chief, and drew up most of the detailed drawings, but it emerged in 1885, when there was a dispute with Deacon over estimated construction costs, that Deacon had been appointed by the corporation as joint engineer. Hawksley felt obliged to resign.

Hawksley had been concerned by the possibility of uplift forces on the dam, and had increased its thickness, and thus its cost. Deacon realized that uplift could be dealt with without a dam of such thickness, by taking account of the bonding of the masonry to the bedrock, and providing a drainage network beneath the downstream face. When completed in 1888 the dam was to enclose the largest man-made reservoir in Europe. It was probably the world's first to take account of uplift, and to incorporate an underdrainage system. It stands today as an effective counter to claims of superior contemporary continental methods of analysis and design of masonry dams. In 1881 and 1895 French-designed dams failed at Habran and Bouzey respectively, demonstrating that the theoretical advances made in the design at Furens were not the complete answer.

NOTES

1. Unattributed contemporary quotation from Ackroyd, P., *Sindaw Stevenson*, 1990, p. 383.
2. E. Chadwick, *The Sanitary Conditions of the Labouring Classes*, HMSO, 1842.
3. J.W. Bazalgette, Evident of 13 July 1888 in *Final report of the Royal Commission . . . into . . . the working of the Metropolitan Board of Works*, (pp. xxix), London, 1889, p. 335.

CHAPTER NINE

Opening Up Australia

Of all our Colonies, none offers fairer prospects of ample returns to the colonist and the mother country than Australia . . .

Sidney's Australia Handbook, *1846.*

Australia differs from all the other inhabited continents in that before the arrival of the first Europeans there was no history of civil engineering. While Africa had the pyramids of Egypt, South America the Inca roads, Aborigine society provided no such monuments to past achievements. From the 1850s when the discovery of gold in Victoria encouraged the import of prefabricated iron buildings for the goldfields and the rapid developments of railways, and brought about an urgent need for adequate water supply and sewerage schemes, civil engineers have played a crucial role in the making of Australia. Bridges and other railway materials were at first imported from the United Kingdom, later Australia began to design and build its own locomotives and equipment. Members of the Institution of Civil Engineers have played an important role in the construction of Australian infrastructure since the early nineteenth century. At first they were involved in a consultative capacity, or as suppliers of machinery for use in the first mills and mines in the continent. Soon members began to take up appointments in Australia, a great impetus being the establishment of Public Works Departments and the coming of the railways in the mid-nineteenth century.

All road development in Australia has occurred since European colonization. Prior to this, there was only a network of Aboriginal footpaths used as trading routes. The first convict transports arrived in Sydney Cove on 26 January 1788. During that year a road to the wharf was completed, as was Australia's first bridge, using timber to cross the Tank Stream at the head of Sydney Cove. Australia's first road was built by convict labour in 1789. The road was 2 km long and ran from Dawes Point to the Governor's residence, via the Tank Stream bridge. The first road of any length

PLATE 60 Manly Beach ferry terminal with *Royal Alfredo* steamer. Prior to the construction of Sydney Harbour Bridge, ferries were the main method of transport around Sydney Harbour. By the end of the nineteenth century they were increasingly unable to cope with the traffic. 13.75 in x 10.25 in. Photographer: J. Sharkey/NSW PWD

was a 25 km route between Sydney and Parramatta, completed in 1791. Like most roads in the new colony, it was mainly used for foot traffic, one reason being a shortage of horses and cattle.

A drought in 1812 which highlighted the colony's lack of access to fertile land prompted an expedition which successfully established a route over the Blue Mountains to the Bathurst region. Australia's first arterial road, built during 1814 by convict labour, linked Sydney and Bathurst over this route, much of which remains today as the Great Western Highway.

The decline in the availability of convict labour in the 1850s, and the advent of the railways, triggered the deterioration of many roads. Rail transport was cheaper and faster, and was free from the competition of an existing road network. Much road construction, apart from in urban areas, became restricted to feeders to railway stations. Similarly, stage coaches, which had begun on the Sydney–Parramatta road in 1818, were reduced to feeder services.

By the middle of the nineteenth century, roads had been constructed in all states. Their condition, however, remained generally poor, with deep mud and ruts. A wide range of construction techniques was used. During the 1820s, McAdam's methods were adopted on some major roads. The first length of macadam road was constructed on the Prospect to Richmond road in New South Wales in 1822, the technology having probably been brought over by military engineers posted to Australia.

Macadamized construction was less popular for urban roads, the interstices between the stones being difficult to clean. In urban areas, particularly Melbourne and Sydney, wooden-block paving was the dominant material; rural roads often consisted simply of a base of planks or logs. Despite the inadequacy of the road network it was not until the discovery of gold in Victoria in 1851 that the first railway was built. This accompanied a gold rush similar to that which occurred in California in 1849, as the working-class population from the other states flocked to the goldfields. The increase in population caused a boom in the building trade, particularly in cities such as Melbourne.

The discovery of gold had a major influence on the prosperity of Victoria and New South Wales, and was especially important in stimulating railway construction from coastal regions into the goldfields, the early lines from Melbourne to Bendigo and Ballarat being good examples of this.

Australia's first steam-worked railway, the Melbourne and Hobson's Bay Railway, opened in Victoria on 12 September 1854. Two miles long, it ran from Melbourne to Port Melbourne, and was built to a gauge of 5 ft 3 in. It originated from the need to improve the transport of supplies to the Victoria goldfields.

Shortly afterwards, on 26 September 1854, the Sydney Railway Company opened the first line in New South Wales, from Sydney to Parramatta. This was a 13 mile long, 4 ft 8½ in gauge line. The simultaneous construction of these two railways, broad gauge in Victoria, standard gauge in New South Wales, marked the beginning of the gauge problems which have bedevilled Australian railways ever since.

The situation arose after the Sydney Railway Company's chief engineer, Francis Webb Sheilds, MInstCE, an Irishman, favoured the Irish broad gauge of 5 ft 3 in, which he persuaded the New South Wales government to adopt. The decision was communicated to the governments of Victoria and South Australia, who then also stipulated broad gauge for their own line, hence its adoption in Melbourne.

However, in 1852, Sheilds resigned suddenly over a disagreement relating to his salary. He was replaced by a Scottish engineer, James Wallace, who favoured George Stephenson's 4 ft 8½ in standard gauge. The Sydney Railway Company reverted to standard gauge, but in Victoria and South Australia, the companies had already ordered broad gauge equipment, and refused to change.

The Sydney–Parramatta line was taken over by the State, renamed the Great Western Railway, and was gradually extended westwards, reaching Bathurst in 1876. The chief engineer was John Whitton. His work involved heavy works to carry the line over the Blue Mountains, notably the Lithgow Valley Zig-Zag. On his retirement in 1890, he left over 2,000 miles of lines open for traffic in New South Wales.

In Victoria, a line from Melbourne (Williamstown) westwards to Geelong was opened throughout on 25 June 1857, and was extended further westwards to provide a 96 mile through route from Melbourne to Geelong in 1862. Another major route was constructed from Melbourne to Bendigo, 101 miles, and completed in 1862, with a further extension to Echuca on the New South Wales border in 1864. A third line ran to Wodonga on the New South Wales border opposite Albury and was completed in 1873. Chief Engineer of Victorian Railways was George Christian Darbyshire from 1856 to 1860, followed by Thomas Higinbotham from 1860 to 1878. Over one thousand miles of line in Victoria were built under his superintendence.

The desire to exploit the new-found mineral and agricultural resources of the country was the main stimulus to railway construction as lines were driven inland to serve the new goldfields and settlements, as was the case, for example, with the line to Bendigo. The territory faced by the early railway surveyors and engineers was extremely hostile. Thomas Griffin, in his paper on the location of railways in Victoria, describes a survey of 14 miles of railway which took two years to complete, due to almost

PLATE 61 Suburban railway station, New South Wales. 13.75 in x 10.25 in. Photographer: J. Sharkey/NSW PWD

impenetrable jungle, great fallen trees and dense undergrowth. Survey parties camped in jungle clearings, and had to carry all their equipment and supplies on their backs, as the ground was too rough for horses.

Railway development in the three remaining states came later: Queensland in 1865, Tasmania in 1871, and Western Australia in 1879. Because of the sparsely populated and difficult terrain, the lines were of economical construction and most were built to the 3 ft 6 in narrow gauge.

The first major intercolonial rail connection was established in 1883, when the New South Wales and Victorian rails met at Albury, the break of gauge point on the border. This permitted a journey between Melbourne and Sydney, with a change of trains. In 1887, Melbourne and Adelaide were linked by the broad-gauge route of the Victorian and South Australian railways.

Despite financial assistance from their Governments the private railway companies of the various states were beset by financial difficulties from the outset. In New South Wales, Victoria, South Australia, and Tasmania, governments took most of the lines over at an early stage: in Western Australia and Queensland, almost all lines were completely state-owned and built.

Australia's first bridges were masonry and timber structures, and the preponderance of these materials continued throughout the nineteenth century. Structural iron and steel had to be imported for many years, and provided much work for British ironmasters who exported bridges, and also prefabricated buildings.

PLATE 62 Survey encampment in Victoria. 6 in x 4 in. Engineer and photographer: T. Griffin

The first bridge, erected in 1788, was a timber log structure across the Tank Stream in Sydney. It was not until the 1830s, when David Lennox, a stonemason who had worked under Telford, built his first bridge, that any notable structures were erected. His first bridge, a 6.2 m span sandstone arch, crossed Lapstone Creek and survives today. Lennox also designed the 37 m span Landsdowne Bridge opening in 1836. Its design is similar to Telford's bridge over the Severn at Over near Gloucester, on which Lennox had worked. Both this bridge and the 1839 Lennox Bridge in Parramatta exist today, but his longest span (46 m) bridge, Prince's Bridge over the Yarra, in Melbourne, was demolished in 1884.

The earliest timber truss bridge in Australia was that over the Jordan River (1842) at Pontville. The early timber trusses were influenced by European continental practice, a Major Mitchell brought models from Hanover in Germany.

Queensland's first bridge, a timber structure, was built in 1827, in Brisbane, three years after the foundation of the colony. The first permanent bridge over the Brisbane River, the Victoria Bridge, was completed in 1874.

Early bridges in Victoria were also of timber, and the first masonry bridge across the Yarra was that of Lennox (1849–50). When it became a separate colony in 1851 a Select Committee was appointed to look into the condition of the roads and drew attention to the poor state of the timber bridges in the state.

Western Australia's first major bridge was a timber structure at Caufield, built in 1835, a year after the colony's foundation. In 1843 the multi-span timber bridge at the Causeway completed the link between Albany and Perth. In South Australia major crossings were required over the Torrens in Adelaide (timber, 1837), and Murray (iron lattice truss, 1879).

The earliest iron road bridge was a three-span bridge in Maitland, New South Wales, built in 1851. This was followed by the iron bowstring truss City Bridge in Adelaide, erected 1854–6. Although some locally-produced iron was used in bridges in 1859 and 1870, the bulk of such ironwork was imported.

Some box girder road bridges had been supplied by Fairbairn for Victoria in 1855, but it was the growth of the railway system which provided the major market for British ironmasters. As the United Kingdom domestic railway demand levelled, the structural ironwork manufacturers turned to colonial markets, and firms such as Handyside, Kennard's, and the Skerne Iron Works exported many bridges.

The Murray Bridge was designed by William Dempsey who was the United Kingdom consultant for South Australian Railways. The ironwork was supplied by Kennard's Viaduct Works at Crumlin. Steel pins were used, and other joints were bolted for

PLATE 63 Murray Bridge, South Australia, *c.* 1879. 11 in x 8.5 in. Engineer: W. Dempsey; ironwork: Kennards

easy erection. The ironwork arrived in 1868, but it was not until 1873 that the bridge was commenced, and it was not completed until 1879. It was initially opened for road traffic, and rails were not laid until 1886.

Other examples of United Kingdom-supplied iron truss bridges are the Murrumbidgee Road Bridge at Hay (New South Wales), designed by Sir John Fowler and supplied by the Skerne Iron Works (1860s) and the Bremer Bridge at Ipswich, Queensland (*c.* 1868) (three 150 ft-spans) which carried road and rail traffic.

The ironwork of the latter bridge was produced by Handyside's, and the bridge was designed by Sir Charles Fox, the British Consultant for the Queensland Railways. The bridge was on the Ipswich–Dalby line designed by A.C. Fitzgibbon, MInstCE, the engineer-in-chief of the Queensland Railways at the time.

By the 1880s Australian engineers were feeling the need for independence from the 'home' country. One of the first engineers to show this was H.C. Mais, who went on a world tour to study foreign practice. The results can be seen on the Adelaide–Nairne

PLATE 64 Adelaide–Nairne Railway, South Australia, *c.* 1882. 17 in x 12.75 in. Engineers: H.C. Mais, C.S. Smith

Railway, where the viaducts clearly reflect American influence.

At the time of its construction in 1888 the original Hawkesbury River Bridge was described as the most important in Australia. It comprised seven spans of 410 ft and was 2,896 ft long. The completion of the bridge in 1889 linked the railway system of New South Wales, previously divided by the Hawkesbury River, and made possible railway communication between Adelaide, Melbourne, Sydney and Newcastle and Brisbane and beyond. Designs were approved by a distinguished committee of Institution members including W.H. Barlow and Sir John Fowler. Although the contract was awarded to the Union Bridge Company of New York, much of the iron and steelwork was fabricated in the United Kingdom, and the resident engineer for the New South Wales Government was C.O. Burge.

Governor Phillips, according to his autobiography *Voyage to Botany Bay* (1789), selected Sydney Cove as the site for the first British settlement because it 'had the finest spring of water'. In fact Phillips was mistaken about the supply available and almost immediately the first settlers had to identify other sources, the

PLATE 65 Nepean River and Tunnel, *c.* 1882. 10.25 in x 7.5 in. Engineers: W. Clark, T.W. Keele; photographer: T.W. Keele

main source being the Tank Stream. It was a major struggle to conserve this source, and pollution became an increasing problem. In 1802 three tanks were excavated from the rock near the mouth of the stream, but they became polluted, and in 1811 a drought exhausted them. Whenever drought followed years of plenty, wells were dug, until in 1827 John Busby, the colony's mineral surveyor, recommended a tunnel be constructed from the Lachlan Swamp to supply the town.

By 1850 the pressure of population was beginning to exhaust supplies. The early 1850s saw a succession of reports, resulting in the decision to take water from the Botany Swamps, via a 30 in-diameter cast-iron rising main, to two service reservoirs, which began operation in 1858. In 1867 further water shortages led to the establishment of a Royal Commission which recommended the Upper Nepean Scheme in 1869. No immediate agreement was possible, however, and it was not until 1876, when the decision was made to appoint William Clark as a United Kingdom consultant, that the problem was resolved. In 1877 his Upper Nepean Scheme was approved, but it took ten years before any water flowed, due to technical and other delays. The scheme involved the construction of an earth dam (Prospect Reservoir) and the diversion of water via tunnels and canals from the Upper Nepean to there.

As with Sydney, a major factor in the choice of Melbourne as the site for an early centre of colonization was proximity to a source of water, in this case the River Yarra. Unlike Sydney, Melbourne's water supply was to prove adequate, although gradually the source of water has moved further up the Yarra and its tributaries. In 1853 Matthew B. Jackson was appointed engineer to supervise the construction of the Yan Yean reservoir, supplied, via a 2-mile aqueduct, from the Plenty River, and a water distribution system was installed in Melbourne which survived into the mid-twentieth century.

Further work was necessary by 1879, and another earth dam was erected at Toorourrong, 1879–86, to supply the Yan Yean Reservoir. A further aqueduct, the Maroondah, was commenced in 1886, supplying Preston Reservoir. Much of this work was carried out by William Davidson and his successor, William Thwaites.

Brisbane's first water supply scheme was the work of Joseph Brady. Brady had earlier worked on the first waterworks scheme for the Victorian mining community of Bendigo (1858).

While the story of the main towns is of interest, it was the rapid development of the mining communities in the 1850s which prompted the major development of water supply elsewhere. Between 1850 and 1865 twenty-four reservoirs were constructed for the mining communities of Victoria, and by the mid-1860s the mining communities of Bendigo, Ballarat and Geelong had efficient public water supply schemes under construction or installed. John Baillie Henderson was responsible for two of these.

The majority of the towns in New South Wales relied upon water supplies pumped from neighbouring rivers, and supplying local reservoirs. These schemes were installed under the supervision of E.O. Moriarty. The mining districts around Newcastle derived their water from the River Hunter, the scheme being designed by William Clark in 1877, somewhat later than their Victorian counterparts.

With increasing understanding of Australia's geography and climate, rural water supply was soon revealed to be a problem. From 1869 wells and tanks were constructed to supply the stock routes of New South Wales. In 1884 a Royal Commission was appointed to study the conservation of water. H.G. McKinney was a leading light in the work, which recommended the keeping of systematic river gauge records, and the construction of irrigation canals in the Murray/Murrumbidgee basins, and further investigation of the Darling basin.

Artesian water was first struck in 1879 at Burke in New South Wales, and J.B. Henderson, who had earlier worked in Victoria, realized its potential importance in Queensland. He worked with the Government Geologist, A.B. Jack, to define the Queensland artesian basin, which was found to underlie two-thirds of the state. Because of extensive pumping, flow began to diminish and Henderson urged controls, which were introduced in 1910. Henderson realized the importance of meteorological information for the water engineer, and his department was responsible for coordinating rainfall and groundwater records. He was responsible for the basis of Queensland's irrigation and water supply schemes as they exist today.

The earliest proposals for a sewerage system in Melbourne date back to 1842, when the City Council was constituted. This body had no power to raise a legally enforceable rate, and nothing was to be achieved for nearly forty years. In 1853 a Board of Commissioners was set up which recommended the construction of a main sewer in Flinsters Street in 1854. Although contracts were invited, and cast-iron plates actually ordered, the unwillingness of the State Government to spend money meant it was not until 1888 that it was possible to force the Government to appoint a Royal Commission. By this time the population was 427,000, and the Yarra must have resembled an open sewer. In 1889 James Mansergh, the famous nineteenth-century public health engineer and an ICE President, was commissioned to make a report on the sewage problem.

Mansergh recommended dividing the city in two, with outfalls at two sewage works, one for each part of the city. His design population was 1.7 million. His proposal was described in his ICE obituary as 'the largest of its kind ever devised'. William Thwaites, who was appointed engineer for the sewer works, recommended that a smaller diameter be used, except in the city centre, and the design population be reduced to one million. He substituted one pumping station/sewage works/outfall for Mansergh's two, and recommended sewers be constructed in the separate system. Thwaites, and his successor C. Kuissmaul, carried through this work which remained the basis of the system well into the twentieth century.

Sydney, like Melbourne, had only a very rudimentary sewage disposal system until the mid-nineteenth century. In 1838–9 pipes were laid down the main streets, but the rock foundations of the town delayed further progress. In 1854 commissioners were appointed and they developed a combined sewerage/surface drainage system, which discharged directly into the harbour. This system was continued by the City Council from 1857, and five main outfalls were used. By the 1870s the pollution of the harbour associated with the growth in population was becoming a menace to public health, and in 1877 a new scheme was adopted. The works were commenced in 1880 under W.C. Bennett and comprised three main outfalls. In 1918 the Metropolitan Board of Water Supply and Sewerage described the resultant scheme as, 'without exaggeration the best in the world!'

CHAPTER TEN

Europe Catches Up

On all these Continental [Railway] lines, it must be observed that though at their commencement the English system was generally adopted, English locomotives and carriages used, and in many cases the work was undertaken by English contractors, yet a short time has sufficed to emancipate them from dependence on this country, and with our tools, and their own natural talent, they in many cases, successfully compete with their tutors.

Sir William Cubitt, ICE Presidential Address, 23 December 1851.

At the close of the Napoleonic Wars the United Kingdom had an impressive technological lead over the rest of Europe. This was reflected particularly in industries such as iron manufacture, steam-engine technology, and textiles. Although in part due to commercial factors, the expertise of British engineers and scientists undoubtedly played a role, as did the skills of the workforce.

In the late eighteenth century engineers such as Rennie and Smeaton had visited the Continent to investigate the skills of continental millwrights, but at the close of the Napoleonic Wars a series of continental visitors came to discover what British engineers were doing – men such as Dupin, Dutens and Navier from France, Gerstner and Kudriaffsky from Austria, Oeynhausen and Dechen from Prussia. Despite embargoes on labour (until 1825) and machinery, British craftsmen and engineers went overseas, and in the first list of ICE members for 1824 members were working in France (iron and gasworks) and Russia (ironworks) as well as the British colonies.

The European market provided an excellent export opportunity for British civil engineers and associated manufacturers, particularly when the railway age began, and contractors such as Mackenzie and Brassey undertook to build many of the Continent's railways.

While the British had a strong technological lead, particularly in manufacturing capacity, in other respects continental civil engineers possessed certain advantages, such as a systematic approach to the education of engineers that had been established early on the Continent. Although natural philosophy was taught in some way, particularly in Scotland, there was nothing in Britain to compare with the École des Ponts et Chaussées and other higher engineering schools in France, or their Spanish and Russian imitators, nor with the technical universities established all over German-speaking Europe in the early nineteenth century.

The use of cast iron in bridges was a largely British phenomenon. When Iron Bridge was erected in 1779 it seized the imagination of Europe. Because the continental capacity to produce cast iron was limited, almost all the early imitations were on a very small scale and of wrought iron. In Britain many hundred cast-iron arch bridges were built, but the Continent never really took them up to the same extent, relying instead on timber, masonry, and wrought iron. There were exceptions, notably the tubular cast-iron arches developed by Polonceau. The most famous example was the Carousel Bridge in Paris, but an example still survives at Seville in Spain. Polonceau originally intended that the tubular cast-iron ribs should be filled with a laminated timber arch, and only at Seville did he place absolute faith in the cast iron.

The story of suspension bridge technology is much more complex. Although suspension bridges are an ancient structural form, and the use of iron in suspension bridges in China and Tibet dates from 206 BC, with use common by the seventh century AD, it was not until the nineteenth century that the level-deck suspension bridge, as we would recognize it today, became an accepted solution to civil engineering problems.

PLATE 66 Polonceau Bridge at Seville, 1880s. 14 in x 6.25 in. Engineer: A.R. Polonceau

PLATE 67 Bergues Suspension Bridge, Geneva. Engineer: G.H. Dufour; photographer: Beguin

In Britain Captain Samuel Brown had developed a patent for wrought-iron cables, and in 1814 Thomas Telford initiated a series of tests on various types of chains and cables for a proposed 1,000 ft-span suspension bridge across the Mersey at Runcorn. Bridges began to be erected in the United Kingdom, and news was spread to the Continent via Dupin and Dutens. Despite the limitations of cast-iron technology on the Continent, wrought iron could be manufactured in sufficient quantities for such structures. Navier was sent from France to report on the phenomenon to the Ponts et Chaussées administration in France. He favoured the use of eyebar cables as used by Telford and Brown, but a manufactury in the south of France owned by the Seguin brothers, realized the commercial potential of wrought-iron wire cables. After erecting a successful trial bridge, their ideas were taken up by G. Dufour, something of a Swiss national hero. Between 1822 and 1836 he designed a series of suspension bridges for Geneva, including the inverted bowstring Bergues Bridge. Unusually for Dufour this used wrought-iron chains rather than the wire he favoured elsewhere. Partly as a result of these endeavours, following a report by Louis Vicat, the French Ponts et Chaussées authorized the use of wire suspension bridges, and in the following twenty years perhaps five hundred were erected, a typical example being that at Avignon. Thus although the earlier work on wire suspension bridges in Europe was carried out by the British, the French were responsible for developing the prototype of the modern parallel-wire suspension bridge as we know it. The peak of the first phase of this achievement was Chaley's bridge at Friburg (1834), at the time of its construction the longest span in the world. Following the failure at Basse-Chaine in 1850 French suspension bridge building virtually ceased and the initiative passed across the Atlantic.

Although with hindsight the French choice of wire cables was justified, this was by no means obvious at the time, and elsewhere in Europe the type favoured by the British held sway. One of the earliest imitators was Bedrich Schnirch, a Czech engineer who was working at the time in the Austrian equivalent of the Ponts et Chaussées. He was responsible for the first chain suspension road bridge on the Continent at Strassnitz in 1823–4, and for the next forty years was involved in the design of suspension bridges in Austria–Hungary. His work should not be regarded as derivative. He was responsible for the world's first suspended roofs, in the 1820s. In 1832 he wrote a theoretical approach to suspension bridge design. In 1842 he designed a twin-deck road/rail suspension bridge and later became involved in developing a means of stiffening suspension bridges against dynamic loads by the use of a Warren truss-type arrangement between the main suspension cables, rather than by the use of a deep deck truss. The first attempt to design a suspension railway bridge, using Samuel Brown's system, had been a failure. Built across the Tees on the Stockton–Darlington Railway it was unstable under the load of a train and had to be immediately propped on trestles. Two bridges were built in Vienna on Schnirch's system, the first being an 83.45 m railway bridge across the Danube Canal in Vienna, opened on 2 September 1860. This was more or less contemporaneous with the Niagara Suspension Bridge, and the two were the only 'successful' railway suspension bridges of the nineteenth century.

Elsewhere in Europe the majority of bridges were based on the British eyebar chain suspension model. Most were designed and built locally, although the important group of suspension bridges built for Russia in the 1820s, utilized an *émigré* group of French, German and British engineers. There were also two notable exceptions in which the ironwork was supplied from England – the Szechenyi Bridge in Budapest, and the Kiev Bridge across the Dniepr. The former was designed by William Tierney Clark, the latter was the work of Charles Blacker Vignoles.

PLATE 68 Aspernbrücke, Vienna. 9.5 in x 7.5 in carbon print. This was the second bridge Schnirch designed with stiffened cables. Engineer: B. Schnirch

The most obvious export achievements of British engineers in the mid-nineteenth century were, however, associated with railways. This was to some extent the result of British financial investment in continental lines, partly because British iron manufacturing was far ahead of the Continent in terms of capacity and technological achievements, and partly because of British expertise in building lines. Continental governments were impressed by the British achievements, and often, in the absence of adequate local capital, railways were financed by the State. As the century advanced this work was increasingly carried out by local engineers and consultants, and the French in particular rivalled the British in designing and building foreign railways.

The most successful names associated with the British achievement were Mackenzie and Brassey, railway contractors. Brassey was involved between 1841 and 1870 in the construction of over 3,000 miles of continental railway. Continental railways were generally built using similar methods to those employed by the British. Construction of railways in the Tyrol was reminiscent of that in the Ghats in India. British contracting interest was maintained when British capital was involved, as with the Francis Canal

PLATE 69 Brennerbahn under construction, 1864–7. 10.5 in x 8 in. Photographer: C.A. Czichna

in Hungary, built by Wythes in the 1870s. In Eastern Europe development tended to be slower and this emerged as an export market for the French in particular. Russia, despite considerable natural resources and a well-established civil engineering profession, was particularly slow in developing self-sufficiency. This was nothing to do with the ability of the engineers, some of whom, such as Jourawski, Belelubsky and Sobko, made important contributions to the development of structural engineering. The Russians were still building American-designed 1840s locomotives in 1860, and using them twenty years later, a testimony to their own backwardness rather than American ingenuity.

German technological progress had been obscured to some extent by political fragmentation. Following the Franco–Prussian War, German railway mileage rivalled that of Great Britain (14,842 miles compared with 16,082 miles) and the German iron and steel industry was challenging Britain in traditional markets like South America. The series of iron bridges across the Rhine and other major rivers demonstrated that German engineers had profited by their studies of British and American technology and French theories. Karl Lentze's six 400 ft-span lattice design for the crossing of the Vistula at Dirschau, opened in 1857, and his contemporary Nogat crossing at Marienburg were undoubtedly influenced by the lattice structures he had seen in Ireland. They were followed by bridges which increasingly demonstrated German mastery of the iron truss, types such as that developed by Heinrich Gerber, an early cantilever, and by Friedrich Pauli, the most famous lenticular truss. Methods of analysis developed by

PLATE 70 Russian-built, American-designed locomotive of 1860. 10.75 in x 8 in. Photographer: T. Urquhart

engineers like Emil Winkler and Otto Mohr retain their importance in soil mechanics and structural engineering today. These developments were contemporary with the emergence of iron founders like Harkorts as major bridge builders in Germany and beyond.

In contracting circles the German achievements have been overshadowed by the work of Gustav Eiffel which gained justifiable renown. Working basically on ironwork construction, Eiffel's team was responsible for some of the greatest engineering achievements of the second half of the nineteenth century: bridges such as the Douro and Garabit viaducts, and structures like the observatory at Nice. Eiffel was successful in bringing together a design team including men like Maurice Koechlin, who were well able to exploit the increased theoretical understanding of structural behaviour and the new analytical techniques of graphic statics. Their most famous achievement was the Eiffel Tower, which in a sense marks the end of an era. It was erected of wrought iron and really marks the end of the iron age, as the use of

PLATE 71 Francis Canal under construction. 10 in x 8 in. Engineer: W.H. Barlow; contractor: G. Wythes

structural steel became increasingly common and the year after the completion of the tower the Forth Railway Bridge, which employed widespread use of steelwork, opened. Eiffel himself became embroiled as contractor in the Panama Canal scandal shortly after.

The designs of Eiffel and his team were only one of several indications that continental engineers were beginning to seize the initiative from their United Kingdom counterparts in the last quarter of the nineteenth century. Concrete, a material with a history almost as old as human civilization, became increasingly popular as a construction material as the nineteenth century progressed, in part due to improvements in cement manufacture. These developments were pioneered in Britain, but continental engineers such as Vicat closely monitored these developments, and by the second half of the century continental manufacturers began to surpass the quality of cement achieved by the British. They began to exploit this material in combination with iron as reinforced concrete. The structural use of this material again seems to have been pioneered by the British – William Wilkinson in Newcastle. Other patents were taken out on the Continent,

PLATE 72 Eiffel Tower under construction, 7 December 1887. 17 in x 15.75 in. Engineer/contractor: G. Eiffel; photographer: Durandelle

PLATE 73 Early reinforced-concrete bridge. From a trade catalogue produced by Wayss. The pioneers of reinforced concrete made extensive use of photographs in the promotion of their products. 7 in x 5 in. Engineer: M. Koenen/Wayss; contractor: Wayss

notably by Joseph Monier, who used the material initially for garden containers. His patents were taken up by Wayss in Germany, and problems of analysis were solved by Mathias Koenen. Among the early structures for which these firms were responsible in Central Europe were bridges which show a surprising lightness of form reminiscent of the later achievements of Robert Maillart.

The increasingly successful use of analytical techniques in civil engineering is again typified by the French in their design of masonry dams in the second half of the nineteenth century. The Furens Dam, which helped provide water for St Etienne, was designed by Graeff and Delocre. It is generally accepted as the first dam to be designed using modern principles of stress analysis. In 1853 Sazilly proposed a method of gravity dam analysis to find the correct profile for a masonry dam. The objective was that at any horizontal section of a dam the maximum vertical pressure stress would be equal whether the dam was empty or full. Graeff and Delocre, when considering Furens, had to decide on a reasonable figure for this stress, and turned to the older existing masonry dams in Spain for design examples. From these they copied the curved form and calculated their existing stresses, and used these to provide the upper and lower design stresses for Furens. While the resultant design was conservative, and ignored tensile stresses and uplift, it stands today as a testimonial to the first engineers to design a dam without reliance on empirical methods.

The greatest achievement of the continental engineers was, arguably, the construction of the transalpine tunnels. Transport tunnelling was nothing new, many canal tunnels having been built in the British Isles in the eighteenth century. Central Europe had a long tunnelling tradition associated with its mining industry. The problems of crossing the Alps were of a different order of scale. As the railway web spread across Europe in the 1850s, the Alps stood in the way of a complete network. Robert Stephenson was called in and pronounced the problem insoluble. The sort of length of tunnel attempted before was only possible above the snow line, and had to be ruled out. The problems to be solved were therefore to identify a suitable route, and then solve the technical problem of drilling through a mountain mass and the problems of ventilation and heat several miles underground.

The first route to be identified, between Italy and France, was the Fréjus (Mont Blanc) Tunnel, with a distance of 40,095 ft between Bardonnèche and Furneaux. The scheme was drawn up by two Italian engineers, Sommeiller and Grattoni. Sommeiller had developed a compressed-air drill from British, American and German precedents. The remote location meant two contractors' villages had to be built for about two thousand men. They were model examples of such communities. At first, excavation was by hand, a painful 91 inches a day for six years. The compressed-air

PLATE 74 Furens Dam. 13 in x 9.5 in. From *Les Travaux Publics de la France*, a massive compilation of photographs taken under the auspices of the Public French Works Department by Baldus and others. Engineer: Graeff & Delocre

tunnelling machine when introduced then permitted progress of about 7.7 inches every twenty-four hours. Ventilation and heat were major problems. Work began in 1857 and the tunnel was completed on Christmas Day 1870. More than 960,000 cubic yd of rock were excavated using 580 tons of gunpowder, with only twenty-eight deaths recorded. It was a model project.

The St Gotthard Tunnel, on the other hand, was a project where everything went wrong. Work began in 1872, with the contractor Louis Favre undertaking to complete the work in eight years, or invoke a penalty clause. Almost immediately problems became obvious: the workings were wet from the first, dust and fumes crippled workers after 3–4 months, the water necessary to power the compressed-air equipment was in short supply, and then hard serpentine rock was encountered. The pressure of the work was too much for Favre who died from a heart attack in the tunnel in 1879. Although breakthrough occurred in 1880, the lining remained to be completed, and this was not achieved until 23 May 1882. A major problem was an area of weak rock which assumed the quality of flowing clay, preventing lining from proceeding until a granite invert was constructed. Despite their achievement the contractors lost 12.45 million francs on the job. The firm was finished. More than 310 deaths and 877 permanent disabilities resulted. But the Alps had been conquered.

CHAPTER ELEVEN

The British in India

In the whole history of governments not excluding that of ancient Rome no alien ruling nation has ever stamped on the face of a country more enduring material monuments of its activity than England has done, and is doing in her great Indian dependency.

G.W. Macgeorge, Consulting Engineer for railways, to the Government of India. Ways and works in India, London, 1894.

The earliest engineering works carried out by the British in India were military works associated with the defence of the East India Company's trading stations on the Subcontinent. The East India Company had had a military presence in India since the seventeenth century, which gradually grew in line with the increase in territorial possessions. Although the company in London exercised overall control via its court of directors in its headquarters in Leadenhall Street, there was a considerable degree of autonomy for the heads of the three presidencies: Madras, Bombay and Bengal. The President or Governor of Bengal was given overall control in India in 1773. With the conquest of much of India in the late eighteenth and early nineteenth centuries, a civil (i.e. non-military) service was developed to administer the territories, with an increasing emphasis on education and training, bringing with it professionalism and a reputation for incorruptability. Each presidency had its own military force, and these included corps of engineers.

The earliest civil engineering schemes were associated with the renovation of the existing perennial irrigation canal network, and date from 1817 when work was commenced on the western Jumna (Yamuna) Canal. The next major public works project was the Grand Trunk Road, conceived under Lord William Bentinck, who was Governor General of Bengal 1828–34, and the first Governor General of India, and planned initially from Calcutta to Delhi, but extended eventually to Lahore. Work began in 1832 under Captain George Thomson of the Bengal Engineers.

When Lord Dalhousie was appointed Governor General of India in 1848 he initiated a fresh programme of public works, and in recognition of the scale of this new commitment a Public Works Department was set up in 1854. Initially this department was staffed by military engineers, particularly officers of the Bengal Engineers. As the century progressed, and the impact of education and a career structure began to be felt, an increasing proportion of engineers were civilian personnel. Military training had been available for some time at the Royal Military Academy (Woolwich) since 1741 and subsequently the company's college at Addiscombe (1809–61); education for civil servants began at Fort William College in Calcutta, and then Haileybury College, Hertfordshire. None of these was really adequate to deal with the training of the number of engineers required for the public works programme. As a result, in 1847 the Thomason College of Civil Engineering was established at Roorkee, followed by further colleges at Calcutta, Madras and Poona. They were particularly successful in training subordinate engineers, including increasing numbers of Indians. To help solve the continuing shortage of well-qualified engineers, the Royal Indian Engineering College, Coopers Hill (Surrey) was set up in 1871. It was from these mixed military and civilian sources that many of the Public Works Department engineers were drawn, the other main source being civil engineers trained in the United Kingdom, largely under the traditional system of pupillage which had been established in the eighteenth century.

This new wave of civil engineering works on the Subcontinent, which in many ways represents the peak of achievement of British civil engineers in the nineteenth century, and a lasting testimonial to the 'beneficial' effects of colonization, coincided with the introduction of photography, and thus contemporary photographs record these achievements. The photographs were largely the work of the civil engineers working on the projects, individuals like John Brunton, engineer to the Scinde Railway, and later the Indus Valley line, building up an album recording some of their work. Brunton relied on his brother, a keen amateur photographer, to take his photographs. Elsewhere it is possible the contractor paid a photographer to record the work to help refute charges of 'scamping'. Government hydraulic works were likewise recorded. This latter does appear to have been the result of offical action, as from the mid-1850s government engineers were being trained in photography.

The photographs which have survived illustrate an important source of work, for professional civil engineers, consultants, contractors, and suppliers during the second half of the nineteeth century, which made a major contribution to this sector of the British economy. Paradoxically, due to the administrative structure of British India, much of the civil engineering work was designed by 'military' engineers.

Railways were advocated for India from the 1830s and in 1842 Charles Blacker Vignoles made a formal report to the East India Company. Further reports followed and in 1849 two railway companies were sanctioned to build 'experimental' lengths of line: the East India Railway Company, originating in Howrah, opposite Calcutta, and the Great Indian Peninsula Railway, in Bombay. The companies employed United Kingdom consultants, as did the East India Company itself, and in addition civil engineers were sent out from the United Kingdom to survey the lines and superintend their construction.

The Indian railways are civil engineering works on a massive scale. They were made possible by the engineering and organizational expertise gained over the previous twenty years of railway building by the British in the United Kingdom and latterly in Europe. The so-called experimental line on the East India Railway, extending from Howrah to Ranigung (121 miles), was longer than the first main line in England: the London–Birmingham (112.5 miles).

The trial lengths were completed on the first two lines by 1855, and in 1854 contracts were signed for the main lines: the East India line 1,000 miles towards Delhi, and two branches of the GIPR, one of 583 miles to the north-east to join the EIR at Jabbulpore, and the other to the south-east to meet the Madras Railway at Ranchur (410 miles).

In the meantime further lines were sanctioned: Bombay, Baroda and Central India Railway (1853, 310 miles), Scinde Railway (1855, 109 miles), Punjab Railway (1856, 240 miles), Madras Railway (1853, 430 miles). Work on these lines was disrupted by the Indian Mutiny of 1857, which incidentally saw the end of the rule of the East India Company and its replacement by the India Office. Despite this temporary setback, which encouraged further investment in the railway system for strategic reasons, India had a vast railway network by 1866 of 3,734 route miles.

Engineering on such a scale provided great opportunities for ironwork suppliers in particular in the United Kingdom. When the first lines were entertained it was proposed that the majority of bridges and viaducts would be of local brick and stone. The civil engineering world of 1850 was full of the achievements of tubular wrought-iron bridges at Menai and Conway, the fruits of detailed testing and scientific endeavour. George Turnbull (1809–89) recommended the use of tubular girder bridges for the East India Railway when he was sent to India in 1850. The British consultant to the company, James Meadows Rendel, was influenced by Charles Head Wild, an engineer of proven mathematical ability, who had worked on the tubular bridges, to investigate the triangular truss system patented by Warren. It was felt that:

> The principle of this bridge has much to recommend it for India. Composed wholly of wrought iron, in comparatively small parts and every part fitted in its place by machinery . . . the ease with which it can be fixed together and taken to pieces again without the slightest injury admits of it being proved in the workshop of the manufacturer, and of it being erected in its permanent position by the most unskilled and indifferent class of mechanics. . . .[1]

After successful testing in Manchester, Rendel advised the adoption of this bridge system and a whole series of 60 ft and 80 ft spans for such bridges were shipped out to India in the 1850s and '60s. Those on the BBCIR were combined with cast-iron screw piles on the system patented by Mitchell, and were up to 86 (60 ft) spans long.

The Warren trusses introduced on Rendel's advice were only a small part of the ironwork shipped out to India at this time. The East India Railway alone was said to have received 65,000 tons of rails, 44,000 tons of chains and 9,000 tons of bridge girders by

PLATE 75 Attock Bridge on the Punjab Northern Railway, under construction, *c.* 1880. 12 in x 9.5 in. Engineers: Sir G. Molesworth, F.L. O'Callaghan; ironwork (for piers): Handyside; ironwork (for the bridge): Westwood Baillie; photographer: F.L. O'Callaghan

PLATE 76 Landsdowne Bridge over the Sukkur, February 1889. 11 in x 8.5 in. Engineers: Sir Alexander Meadows Rendel, F.E. Robertson; photographer: S.J. Direcha

1859. A single company like Westwood Baillie & Company supplied 2,000 tons of bridge girders between 1856 and 1858. The earliest Warren trusses were exported from Charles Mare's works in Blackwall in 1853, for single track bridges, and erected in 1854. Although many of these trusses were eventually replaced and complaints were heard about the 'great tendency to vibration' and joints working loose, some spans were reused in the next generation of State Railways in the 1870s and '80s, notably the Nizam's State Railway (Hyderabad) which reused some of the 'BBCIR' spans.

Some of the rivers in India were of sufficient span to deter engineers from attempting to bridge them, such as the 'Hooghly' at Calcutta. In the 1880s some major crossings were at last attempted, such as the Attock Bridge in the Punjab, and the Lansdowne Bridge over the Sukkur. The latter was at the time of its opening the longest cantilever bridge in the world, and incidentally described as the ugliest.

Bridging the broad Indian rivers was only one of the engineering achievements of the Indian railways, and arguably the greatest achievement of all was the construction of the Great Indian Peninsula Railway through the Ghats outside Bombay. Robert Stephenson was the United Kingdom consultant and James John Berkley (1819–62) was Chief Engineer in India. Berkley's brother George (1811–93) succeeded Stephenson as United Kingdom consultant on his death in 1859. To the north-east the railway climbed the 9¼ mile Thul Ghat incline, which was built 1857–64, completed under Robert W. Graham, and to the south-east the Bhore Ghat incline, 15½ miles long, built 1856–63. These works included tunnels, masonry viaducts with major earthworks and steep inclines, and involved a workforce of over forty thousand of which nearly a third died, including James Berkley.

These were the first railway works to be photographed in India. The techniques depicted in the surviving photographs of the Bhore Ghat are similar to those one would have expected in any line in the British Isles at the time, which is hardly surprising when one considers that the same consultants and contractors were responsible.

The early work was carried out using traditional English-style contracts. British 'gangers' were regularly striking or otherwise abusing the native workforce. The then Governor of the Bombay Presidency, Sir Bartle Frere, ordered any ganger or other European on the works striking the natives to be instantly dismissed, and forfeit their prepaid return passage. The effect was

PLATE 77 Khandalla station, Bhore Ghat India, Great Indian Peninsula Railway. 9.75 in x 7.75 in. Engineers: J.J. Berkley & R.W. Graham; contractor: Tredwell; (Institution of Mechanical Engineers)

less dramatic than had been hoped, as Sir Bartle himself discovered when he happened upon some part of the construction site on the Ghats. Addressing the English navvy in charge Sir Bartle enquired:

'Well my good man, you appear to be the manager here.'

'Yes sir.'

'And how are you getting on?'

'Oh, sir, we are getting on very well'

'How many natives have you under your orders?'

'Well sir, about 500 of 'em altogether.'

'Do you speak their language?'

'No sir, I don't.'

'Well then, how do you manage to let these natives understand what they are to do?'

'Oh, sir, I'll tell you, I tell these chaps three times in good plain English, and then if they don't understand that, I takes the lukii (stick) and we get on very well'[2]

On enquiry it transpired the man was kindhearted, and much loved by his workforce! The Ghat contracts were among the few successfully completed under the English contracting system. Problems of supervision led to much scamping and in one notorious episode when number 12 contract on the GIPR was opened to traffic the masonry piers of the bridges and viaducts began to crack and tumble. The masonry work was designed to comprise coursed rubble face work with rubble backing, with long stones or 'binders' tieing the facework with the backing. For the system to work it relied on high quality mortar and adequate 'binders'. A level of supervision was required to ensure the mortar was of high standard, and not allowed to dry out too quickly in the heat, and the 'binders' were satisfactory. Resident engineers could not supply the level of supervision required, and in the case of this contract the contractor's work was not up to specification. Incidents such as this, and an increasing number of contractors failing to meet obligations, led from 1867 to most contracts being carried out by direct labour. In India some engineers felt that the influence of the large contractors and United Kingdom consultants prevented the system being abandoned earlier.

By 1869 more than 5,000 miles of strategic railway lines had been built under British superintendence in India, and the network was taken over by the Government of India; by the end of the century the total had doubled.

Despite the export opportunities for the British firms, much of the work was achieved by Indian labour, and one of the first tasks was the establishment of railway workshops so that locomotives and rolling stock could be built and repaired on the Subcontinent. They laid the foundations of the emergence of India as an industrial power.

Major attempts were also made during this period to alleviate problems associated with the seasonal nature of much of India's rainfall, both in terms of providing a perennial supply of irrigation water, and providing adequate pure water supplies for the vast and quick-growing urban population. The first major new canal was the Ganges Canal built between 1842 and 1854 to the designs of Sir Proby Cautley. Although the design was much criticized, partly because its relatively steep fall caused erosion problems, it was a tremendous engineering achievement, irrigating an area, when completed, of 1.3 million acres, a total surpassed only by the 1.6 million on the Chenab Canal of 1883–92. Extensive remodelling was carried out in the 1860s and '70s, and the Lower Ganges scheme was carried out in 1872–8, which added a further 1.244 million acres. These schemes involved massive hydraulic structures such as the Narora Weir on the Lower Ganges Canal, with an overall length of 4,244 ft and width of 180 ft. There was a gradual refinement in design as experience and theoretical understanding improved. Traditional Indian foundation methods – building circular masonry wells as foundations – were refined, with the Solani Aqueduct on the Ganges Canal being built on huge blocks 20 ft square sunk 20 ft below the weir bed. As experience grew loose stone weirs (anicuts) and boulder weirs were built, such

PLATE 78 Narora Weir, Lower Ganges Canal. 10.5 in x 8 in. Engineer: W. Jeffreys

PLATE 79 Solani Aqueduct, Ganges Canal, *c.* 1860. 9.25 in x 7.25 in. Engineer: Sir Proby Cautley; photographer: T.G. Glover

as that at Okhla, resting directly on the sand of the river bed, with well-block foundations for the stones. Seepage through sand in such structures was likely to prove a problem and there were several failures due to undermining, as at Narora in March 1898. By charging for use of the irrigation water these massive public works were generally self-financing in the long term, and in the 1860–1 famine these works proved their value.

Water was also a problem in urban areas, and in the second half of the nineteenth century the authorities in India employed United Kingdom consultants who had gained experience in dealing with the water supply problems of the urban areas of Britain, to introduce water supply schemes in the major cities of the Subcontinent. The characteristic method involved the construction of earth embankment dams using puddle clay cores as had been developed by British engineers like Telford, Leslie and Bateman. One of the most urgent problems was presented at Bombay with its island site and, following the annual monsoon, a virtual nine-month drought. The result was a shortage of water every five years by the 1840s. Moreover, water was being collected in all sorts of shallow containers and tanks became prone to pollution, and cholera an increasing problem.

Two military engineers, Captain Crawford and Lieutenant Delisle, suggested a reservoir at Vehar. These proposals were put to Henry Conybeare who had recently arrived in Bombay as Superintendent of Repairs, in December 1852. Initially he was concerned about evaporation rates from a reservoir in India, but after further work, he supported the idea of a reservoir at Vehar.

PLATE 80 Nagpur goods yard, Nagpur and Chmattisgarh Railway. *c.* 1882. 11 in x 8.5 in. Engineer: J.L. Collings; photographer: J.L. Collings (?)

In 1855 Conybeare returned to England where he prepared plans for a main dam with two saddle dams, all with puddle cores, the largest being 84 ft high and 835 ft long, with an overall storage capacity of 10,800 million gallons. Conybeare never returned to India, and the cores for the saddle dams were omitted during construction, necessitating remedial work and their insertion in 1870–1. Despite this setback the precedent had been set and over the next thirty years more than twenty major earth dams were constructed in India, providing water to all the main towns.

At Nagpur the scheme was slightly unusual in that Alexander Binnie selected as the reservoir site one previously used by the native royal family for a water scheme for their palace and friends in the late eighteenth century. A puddle trench was constructed through the existing earth embankment, which was raised by 17 ft 4 in. The result was that the capacity of the reservoir was increased from 80 million cubic ft to 257 million. Work was carried out by petty contractors, day labourers and prisoners.

A pure water supply was often linked to an adequate sewerage system, and for much of the nineteenth century little was done to tackle problems of sewage disposal. In most towns soil was collected at night and trenched on the outskirts of towns. To deal with problems of contaminated water supply, increasingly remote sources were used as at Calcutta where from 1870 water was piped from 20 miles up river at Pulta.

Because of its location on the Hooghly, by the late eighteenth century Calcutta was being likened to an undrained swamp. By the 1850s it was clear something had to be done about the water supply

PLATE 81 Nagpur Waterworks, puddle core for dam under construction, *c.* 1870. 11.25 in x 8.5 in. Engineer: Alexander Binnie; photographer: J.R. Morris

and sewage disposal problem. A system was designed by William Clark in 1857 based on British experience. From 1859 onwards a network of brick egg-shaped sewers was installed, and by 1875 35 miles of brick and 37 miles of pipe sewers were in place, the sewers draining by gravity to Palmers Bridge pumping station. There the sewage was pumped into a high level sewer with an outfall at Salt Lake approximately 8,000 ft to the east of Calcutta. In 1882 a separate system for discharge of stormwater was developed. By 1884 the system of drainage was more or less complete, but within a few years the suburban growth of Calcutta had outstripped the network, and in 1897 new works had to be commenced.

In Bombay, as in Calcutta, the public health situation had become intolerable by the 1850s. While Calcutta's problems were related to its riverside location, Bombay's stemmed from its growth on a site of seven separate islands. The area between had gradually been reclaimed until there appeared to be only one island, separated by an open ditch or main drain. From 1824 onwards this was gradually culverted, but had no proper gradient to it, and sewage lay stagnant in it for long periods. In 1853 Henry Conybeare suggested draining the sewage into a pit in the dry season, from where it could be used for irrigation purposes. This did not prove to be a solution, and in the 1860s a series of schemes for a drainage system linked to an outfall were put forward. Although some work was carried out, and a pumping station erected at the incongruously named 'Love Grove' in 1867, it was not until 1878 that a scheme with separate drainage for stormwater and sewage was agreed. By 1881 the main drains were completed: 4.25 miles of oval-shaped brick sewers. Despite this, much work remained to be done as late as the 1890s.

It was really in the period 1890–1900 that other major cities like Madras, Benares, and Karachi developed their sewerage systems. As Carkeet James, former engineer in Bombay, remarked in 1917, 'Until comparatively recent years, open drains at the sides of streets, that depended on the monsoon rains for this annual cleansing, constituted the only drainage system existing in many important Indian cities and towns. . . .'[3]

For many, arriving in India was an invigorating, not to say, hazardous experience. At Madras in 1870 the engineer F. (J.E.) Spring, 'had the grim satisfaction of watching many of his fellow-passengers being landed through the surf with their luggage . . . Many years later . . . he had to land or embark himself and his horses in similar surf-boats at various harbourless ports up and down the coast – usually an exciting experience emphasised by lifebelts.'[4] The combination of bars, sand accretion and large rivers made most ports unsuitable for larger vessels, and Robertson's tour of Indian harbours in 1871–2 makes depressing reading. Describing Dhollera, with its mud bunder or jetty at Koonbunder, as, 'without exception, the most wretched looking spot it has ever been my lot to visit',[5] he felt many ports were so poorly located as to be unsuitable for major expenditure on improvements.

This want of adequate harbour accommodation persisted into the early twentieth century, and Sir Guildford Molesworth remarked in his Presidential Address to the ICE in 1904 that, 'there was no port between Calcutta and Bombay where a large vessel could directly discharge its cargo on to a wharf'. This broad generalization ought not to diminish what was achieved. In Bombay and Calcutta improvements were discussed from the 1850s, and in Bombay in particular much was done. At Calcutta, aside from the construction of Diamond Harbour and improvement works at the mouth of the Hooghly, four jetties were built before the Port Trust was established in 1870. In the following ten years a further four jetties were added, but this exhausted the available riverside accommodation and between 1884 and 1890 Kidderpur Docks were built.

Works at Karachi were also successful. Karachi was the natural port for the Punjab and the Sind, being the only port for 500 miles in each direction, although problems of a bar rendered it unfit for any except small native craft.

Following the British takeover of the Sind in 1843 there was strong pressure for action. In 1856 James Walker was consulted and in 1858 he and William Parkes prepared a plan including docks and basins. Work began in 1860 under the supervision of W.H. Price, but finance was not initially sanctioned for the whole project, leading to suspension of work between 1866 and 1868. By 1874 the work was more or less complete. The most interesting feature was the Mamora breakwater which was the first instance of the use of sloping concrete blockwork placed by overhead 'Titan' cranes. Although damaged by storms before completion, the breakwater and harbour works were generally successful, and larger vessels were able to use the port.

Blockwork design was further developed, notably by Sir John Coode, as seen in his proposal for Colombo which was approved in 1873. The 4,712 ft breakwater was built by direct labour under John Kyle's supervision and took ten years (1875–85) to complete.

PLATE 82 Depositing concrete in bags weighing 10 tons each on the sea berm at Columbo, March 1884. Engineer: Sir John Coode; photographer: John Kyle (?)

Additional bond within the breakwater was achieved by filling joggle grooves between the blocks with concrete in bags, and capping the breakwater with mass concrete. A notable feature of this breakwater was that, apart from the stone, everything was imported from the United Kingdom. Coode took great satisfaction in using a photograph to demonstrate the stability of the works in a storm when the harbour was discussed at ICE in 1886. The success of these works can be gauged by the 1,000,000 tons increase in tonnage of shipping using the harbour within a year of the works' completion.

In contrast, the works at Madras were not a success. The breakwater, besides sustaining damage, failed adequately to protect the shipping. In the late 1850s a 1,100 ft long screw pile pier was erected, designed to project beyond the surf to facilitate the unloading of cargo, but this was only partially successful, and did nothing to help larger vessels. In 1868 plans for a harbour were first put forward, and developed by William Parkes. Work began formally in 1877, but the breakwaters, modelled on that at Karachi, were damaged in a cyclone in 1881. Even when completed they offered no protection to ships from the wind, and large vessels had to continue to unload on to lighters in exposed conditions. These problems were not solved until the twentieth century.

NOTES

1. Letter from Rendel–Noad, India Office Library Records, 1 March 1851.
2. J. Brunton, *John Brunton's Book*, Cambridge: University Press, 1939, pp. 106–7.
3. C.C. James, *Drainage problems of the east*, 1917, p. 1.
4. F.J.E. Spring, 'The remodelling and equipment of Madras harbour', ICE *Minutes of Proceedings*, vol. 190, 1912, p. 91.
5. G. Robertson, Second series of reports on Indian harbours, 1873, p. 39.

CHAPTER TWELVE

From East to West: America Takes the Lead

Type of the modern – emblem of motion and power – pulse of the continent.

Walt Whitman, 'To a locomotive in winter', 17 February 1876.

In America a railway is like a river, and is regarded as the natural channel of civilization. Extended into a thinly populated district, it is the pioneer of civilization.

James Hodges.

Civil engineering in North America in the nineteenth century was based on a mixture of home-grown solutions to the problems of scale posed by the vast continent, and the influence of successive waves of European-trained immigrant engineers. While some American engineers, such as Ellet and Strickland, visited Europe to acquaint themselves with the latest ideas and practice, in the second half of the century there was also a steady stream of European engineers such as Ghega, Cuhlmann and Malezieux, who visited America to see the latest practice there. In the second half of the century American engineers became involved in major overseas projects, particularly South American railways, but the tradition had been established much earlier by men such as George Washington Whistler, who was engineer on the first Russian railway from Tsarskoe Selo (Pushkin) to St Petersburg.

The distances involved, and the size of the physical obstacles, inevitably resulted in structures and engineering on a massive scale. They also encouraged an innovative approach to design solutions. Materials which were frowned upon on aesthetic, durability, or cost grounds in Europe might represent the cheapest and most appropriate solution, particularly where transportation costs and difficulties could be a considerable barrier to the use of 'ideal' materials.

In bridge engineering the Americans proved particularly successful in developing practical designs. The abundance of wood encouraged the development of timber truss bridges, and shortages of skilled workmen encouraged a simple approach that any local carpenter could master. Although there was a strong tradition of timber bridge construction in Europe, particularly in Germany and Switzerland, American engineers developed a whole series of truss forms which proved extremely popular, none more so than the Howe Truss. This used a combination of timber and wrought iron and was used throughout Europe and the Americas, and was arguably the most successful bridge patent ever. The development of such forms attracted the notice of European engineers with a more theoretical approach, such as Cuhlmann, and inspired much development in Europe. American engineers such as Whipple and Haupt developed means of calculating the forces in such bridges. There were problems of durability and susceptibility to fire damage with timber bridges, and as iron manufacture expanded, iron truss forms were developed. One of the earliest was that of Wendel Bollman, an engineer on the Baltimore and Ohio Railway. His first all-iron design was at Saraq Factory, Maryland (1850). The Winchester span on Harpers Ferry Bridge was completed in 1851 and in 1852 Bollman patented his system. Eventually, as a result of Civil War damage, all the spans at Harpers Ferry were built to his model. They remained in

PLATE 83 Victoria Tubular Bridge over the St Lawrence, 1860s. The construction of this bridge was photographed by William Notman, a Montreal photographer. This was possibly the first detailed photographic record of bridge construction. Engineers: R. Stephenson and A.M. Ross; ironwork: Canada Works, Birkenhead; contractors: Brassey Peto & Betts; source: Stereocard, (J.G. James Collection)

main-line service until 1894, and some continued to be used as road bridges until floods swept them away in 1936. Despite the success of Bollman and others the predominant bridge material remained timber, with 85.5 per cent of railway bridges being timber compared with 8.5 per cent iron in 1888.

While in the United States of America there was clearly much independence of European influence from the start of the nineteenth century, in Canada such innovation was rarer. Although engineers such as John By and John MacTaggart adopted 'North American' solutions to the problems of early nineteenth-century Canada with their pragmatic approach to construction problems on the Rideau Canal in the 1820s, the railways in particular showed the influence of British engineers. In part this was the effect of British shareholders on the boards of the railways, and also the colonial influence of the British Government. The tubular bridge across the St Lawrence was in many ways a triumph of British engineering, with the ironwork designed according to the system developed by Stephenson and his colleagues for the

PLATE 84 View of Keefers Viaduct on the Canadian Pacific Railroad, *c.* 1886. 9.25 in x 7 in. Engineer: Sandford Fleming

Britannia Bridge, and fabricated in Birkenhead for export. It was from the first a controversial project, with much criticism of its cost, and the availability of cheaper solutions using truss spans. With Canada's proximity to the United States of America, American engineers and ironmasters were able to gain increasing influence. The timber viaducts on the Canadian Pacific Railway were typical of structures to be found on American railways, and were criticized on similar grounds. Sandford Fleming, engineer to the Intercolonial Railway, had to make a personal stand to get much-needed iron trusses adopted on that railway. The long-span iron truss bridges were supplied by United States firms, with the British (Fairbairns) only supplying shorter-span plate girders and lattice trusses.

In the first half of the nineteenth century canal construction and river navigation remained an important part of civil engineering in North America. This was a reflection of the undeveloped nature of the American transport system of the time, the abundance of water, both in the Great Lakes area, and the rivers of the East and Central States, and the fact that they offered natural routes to the interior. Early railways were often designed as feeders or links between the water system. They might be used where inclined planes or similar devices were inappropriate. Despite this the sheer distance involved made some of the early American railways major civil engineering enterprises, and the route mileage of American railways by mid-century had outstripped that of canals, and of Great Britain.

Political pressure after the American Civil War encouraged the completion of the transcontinental links between the Atlantic and Pacific coasts, with the last spike being driven at Promontory

PLATE 85 Colorado Canyon survey, 1884. 8 in x 6 in. Engineer: R.H. Stanton; photographer: F.A. Nims

Point, Utah on 10 May 1867, between the Central and Union Pacific railways. Similar motives encouraged the link between the British Columbia and eastern Canadian seaboards in the 1870s, and led to the building of the Canadian Pacific Railway, with its last spike driven on 7 November 1885. Such civil engineering achievements are world famous. The very real problems involved in surveying such lines are often overlooked. In 1889 a survey party set out to demonstrate the practicability of building a railway along the Colorado River Valley. Within days the party had to return, the chairman of the railway company having drowned. When the party set out again almost immediately there were further accidents, and the official photographer had to return, injured, leaving the civil engineer, Stanton, to complete the survey and the photographs. The railway was never built.

Although the great period of American structural engineering dates from the period after the Chicago fire of 1871, much innovation and achievement predated this. Prefabricated iron homes were only one aspect of the increasing use of iron in buildings from mid-century onwards. Engineers such as Daniel Badger and James Bogardus designed iron-framed structures, and Ward and Ransome began to develop the use of concrete in the 1870s and '80s. Some of the most famous symbols of America – the Capitol building and the Statue of Liberty – made extensive use of structural ironwork, although the Statue of Liberty is a testimony to French ingenuity and Eiffel's genius. The Capitol building made extensive use of iron with cast-iron columns, window frames, and internal fittings, and wrought-iron roof trusses. Its most notable engineering feature was its dome. This was supported on cast-iron trusses resting on cast-iron columns, with the outer form of a crescent-shaped truss taking the profile of the dome. It was designed by August Schoernborn, with Montgomery Meigs responsible for its construction. At the time of its construction the only precedent was St Isaac's Dome in St Petersburg.

Aside from the skyscraper, the most famous achievement of the Americans was the level-deck suspension bridge. There seems little doubt that the level-deck suspension bridges built by Judge Finley at the opening of the nineteenth century acted as the catalyst which resulted in the spread of suspension bridges across Europe in the 1820s. The developments were taken up by Charles Ellet Jr, and John Roebling. Roebling was a German engineer who, having trained in Europe, emigrated to the United States in 1831, and after a brief foray into agriculture, returned to engineering. In 1841 he set up a wire rope manufactory. Roebling was able to build on his civil engineering education to persuade clients that his wire ropes could be used in suspended structures. After the Pittsburg Aqueduct on the Pennsylvania Canal in 1844–5, he won further contracts and became involved in increasing rivalry

PLATE 86 Capitol building under construction. Engineers: A. Schoernborn, M. Meigs; photographer: M. Meigs (?)

with Ellet. Ellet had visited Europe in 1830–2 and seen suspension bridges under erection in France. On his return he had become an unceasing advocate of the suspension bridge. His first proposal for a bridge across the Potomac was submitted in 1832. It was turned down. Throughout the 1830s, while he worked on major canal and railroad schemes, he continued to promote suspension bridges. Despite problems with some of his bridges he was probably responsible for keeping the tradition alive in the United States. His first successful design was at Fairmount (1842). The two rivals corresponded and competed for successive bridge schemes, culminating at Niagara in a joint rail and road scheme. Ellet was initially successful in winning the design, but after the first cables and a temporary bridge had been erected, he fell out with the railway company, and Roebling completed the 821 ft-span structure in 1855.

The Niagara scheme, because of its spectacular location, won widespread fame for Roebling. The fact that he had built the first successful combined rail/road suspension bridge gave the structure added importance. It also meant his reputation has tended to overshadow that of Ellet. Ellet, however, was at the same time involved in the erection of another bridge, the Wheeling, which

PLATE 87 Niagara Falls Suspension Bridge, 1860s. Engineer/ contractor: J.A. Roebling; photographer: J.P. Soule

was built 1847–9, and with a span of over 1,000 ft was the first in the world to exceed that length. In 1854 it was damaged by a great storm and had to be rebuilt. Ellet was unfortunately killed in the American Civil War and his full potential as a designer of suspension bridges may never have been realized. Roebling went on, however, to design the East River or Brooklyn Suspension

PLATE 88 East River (Brooklyn) Bridge under construction, 1878. 'A great work of art, and a successful specimen of advanced bridge engineering, this structure will forever testify to the energy, enterprise, and wealth of that community which shall secure its erection' (J.A. Roebling). Engineers contractor: J.A. & A. Roebling

Bridge. Longer than any other suspension bridge at the time of its completion in 1883, it has always been considered a triumph of civil engineering and Roebling conceived it as such. He was appointed engineer in 1867, and proposed a record-breaking 1,500 ft span. He died after an accident on the bridge site in 1869, and his son Washington was responsible for the completion of the bridge.

Washington Roebling had visited Europe prior to his father's death, and like him was aware of European engineering developments. His particular brief had been to study compressed-air foundations, and the Brooklyn Bridge, along with the St Louis Bridge, was the first in America to make use of pneumatic caissons.

The bridge across the Mississippi at St Louis is now known as the Eads Bridge in memory of its designer. James Buchanan Eads was one of several engineers who made their reputations in dealing with the problems of navigation on the Mississippi. In 1867 he submitted his proposals for a bridge across the river at St Louis; a site for which Ellet had earlier suggested a suspension scheme. They involved an unprecedented main arch span of 515 ft and two side spans of 497 ft, and featured tubular ribs of steel. In the event chrome steel was used for these. Although tubular metal arches had been used by Polonceau some thirty years before, their use had been relatively rare and on a much smaller scale. The use of steel was also rare at this time, although the first instance of its use was more than forty years earlier in the Karlsbrücke Suspension Bridge in Vienna (1828). However, such European influence as there was seems to have been from the Coblenz Bridge. The St Louis Bridge presented major foundation and erection problems. To solve the problems of the foundations pneumatic caissons were used. The major erection problem was to fit the tubes together, using adjustable closing pieces specially designed by Eads. The job took nearly three days' continuous effort, involving packing the tubes in ice in a vain attempt to get the members to fit. The bridge was designed for rail and road traffic, and formally opened on 4 July 1874.

PLATE 89 Eads Bridge, St Louis, under construction. 11.5 in x 8 in. 'It is easy to prove ... that in no other form would the material in these members of your bridge which impart to it the chief feature of its gracefulness be used with such economy' (J.B. Eads). Engineer: James Buchanan Eads; contractor: Keystone Bridge Company; photography: Autotype

Distance between towns was often the chief problem faced by the American civil engineer. In the East, however, population growth meant water supply provided an increasing challenge. By 1800 New York had exhausted local sources of supply, and a succession of distinguished early American engineers – De Witt Clinton, Canvass White and David B. Douglas – developed a scheme to supply the city from a tributary of the Hudson, the Croton. All had considerable experience with canals, Douglas being responsible for the use of inclined planes rather than locks on the Morris Canal. In the event, the work was carried out by another canal engineer, John Bloomfield Jervis.

The scheme involved damming the Croton partly with a masonry dam, partly by use of an earth embankment. The first embankment failed, and Jervis extended the masonry structure to a length of 270 ft. An aqueduct 41 miles long brought the water into New York via sixteen tunnels, the longest being 1,263 ft, and several masonry aqueducts. Water first flowed in 1842, but the scheme was not completed until 1848. By 1856 it was clear the water supply was insufficient and two 90 in-diameter cast-iron pipes were installed by the new engineer, A. Craven, in the 1860s to solve the problem. Further extensions followed in the 1880s, when the New Croton Aqueduct was built. Completed in 1893 it included a 30-mile water tunnel, the longest in the world.

While New York was well established by the 1840s, Washington, DC was a new town. A sound water supply was required for the federal capital, and Montgomery Cunningham Meigs, a graduate of the US Military Academy in 1836, was appointed

PLATE 90 'In the tunnel heading by electric light', New Croton Aqueduct, New York Water Supply, *c.* 1886. This early example of civil engineering photography underground was more or less contemporaneous with Carey's attempts to photograph men inside the caissons of the Forth Railway Bridge. 8 in x 5.5 in. Engineer: Benjamin S. Church; contractors: John Brunton & Co., O'Brien & Clark; photographer: C.F. Ferrer/ Photogravure Company

PLATE 91 Cabin John Branch Aqueduct, Potomac Water Supply, under construction. Engineer: M. Meigs; photographer: M. Meigs (?)

engineer in 1852. Although also responsible for the Capitol building, and subsequently Quartermaster General in the American Civil War, he always took particular pride in the Washington aqueduct. Water was brought from the Potomac Falls. The most notable engineering feature was the Cabin John Branch Bridge, which had a 220 ft span, and for fifty years was the longest masonry arch in the world.

Across the continent on the west coast, one of the sights of San Francisco today is its recently-refurbished cable-car system. Cable traction was one of the earliest forms of rail traction, yet it was in San Francisco where it was most widely applied. In the early years of steam railways cables worked by stationary steam engines were installed whenever there was concern over locomotives being unable to tackle steep gradients. Examples were on the Canterbury and Whitstable Railway (1830), and Liverpool and Manchester Railway (Edge Hill to Wapping, Crown Street and Lime Street). The London–Blackwall Railway was also cable-worked when first opened. By the second half of the century, as locomotive power increased, such a method became increasingly

PLATE 92 San Francisco Cable Car, Haight Street, *c.* 1889. 9.5 in x 7.5 in. Photographer: Flagor

unnecessary. Problems of steep gradients remained, however, and for mountain railways a variety of systems was developed. As San Francisco spread up the nearby hills public transport became a problem. Horses slipped when they pulled their street cars up the inclines. Andrew Smith Hallidie, an engineer who had a wire rope manufactory, took out a patent in 1870 for grips and a pulley to transmit power from engines to a rope to prevent slippage. He developed the idea further. In 1871 he secured financial support, and a trial cableway was built in Clay Street. On 1 August 1873 a length of 3,000 ft, with a maximum gradient of 1 in 6.15, was opened.

Initially capital costs deterred competitors but by the 1890s there were eight companies and more than 25 miles of track. The idea spread to twenty-eight American cities, and back to Europe.

CHAPTER THIRTEEN

Latin America: All That Glisters is not Gold

. . . when we saw all those cities and villages built in the water and the great towns on dry land, and that straight and level causeway leading to Mexico, we were astonished. . . . It was all so wonderful that I do not know how to describe this first glimpse of things never heard of, seen or dreamed of before.

Bernal Diaz, The Conquest of New Spain, (*Penguin classic translation*).

Today Latin America is part of the Third World, with massive economic and social problems and chronic political instability; in the mid-nineteenth century it contrasted favourably with Africa and, to a lesser degree, North America. It had long and close political links with Spain and Portugal, and, despite these, well-established trading links with the rest of Western Europe. When the region gained independence in the early nineteenth century it gained much help from the British and also from the United States with their insistence, in the Monroe doctrine of 1823, that no new European power should dominate. With no direct colonial relationship, much of South America, unlike other areas of the world, could provide a valuable source of work for civil engineers of several nationalities. Its fabled mineral wealth made it a considerable magnet for foreign investment and engineers.

For much of the nineteenth century the myth of El Dorado inspired foreign investment in Latin America, and encouraged the development of civil engineering schemes which might otherwise have been ignored as pipe-dreams. Mining engineers were among the first to be attracted. Railways, with their strong links with mining, inevitably followed. In addition to railways, with major distances and mountain ranges to tackle, harbour and public health schemes were involved, as well as the ongoing search for a satisfactory Atlantic–Pacific link across Central America.

In what increasingly became regarded as the USA's backyard, American engineers were able to demonstrate their skills to an extent seldom seen outside the USA itself. The British were helped in the 'post-colonial' era by their support for the newly independent states, who took inspiration in part from the 'democratic' institutions of the British Isles. In the early nineteenth century distinguished English engineering figures lost their way in the Latin American jungle, notably Richard Trevithick and Robert Stephenson. Both became involved in South American mining concerns. Trevithick was virtually reduced to a pauper and Stephenson discovered that the latest in equipment and technology were rendered useless by problems of transport and geography in the mountains of Venezuela.

Despite the lesson of Trevithick and Stephenson, British engineers, contractors, suppliers and investors were willing to pursue their individual El Dorados in the mid-nineteenth century, as the new states sought a modern infrastructure. A whole host of peripatetic engineers accepted the challenge of mountain and jungle, and were responsible for a system which has survived often virtually unchanged for a century. Mountain and jungle, as in Panama, provided a major barrier to the civil engineer. Pre-Colombian civilization left a civil engineering heritage which demonstrated an infrastructure was possible, even in the mountains. The Inca roads in the Andes overcame communication problems of a severity seldom found elsewhere in the world.

To introduce more modern technology to the continent proved, however, to be a slow process. Early attempts to float railways failed, and the first was not opened until 1848, when a short length was opened in British Guiana, in the neighbourhood of Georgetown. The early period of railway construction began in the 1850s when governments began to provide satisfactory loan guarantees to foreign investors, and European and American engineers and suppliers looked for new opportunities. The first public railway built in Peru between 1850 and 1857 from Callao to Lima, was owned by a Peruvian and an Englishman who nightly divided the profits between them. This followed an American-owned mineral line in Chile built 1849–52 between Caldera and Coprapo.

Many of the railway schemes had distinguished United Kingdom consultants: Edward Woods, for the Central Argentine Railway and extensions to the Caldera–Coprapo line; James Brunlees, for the Brazilian Sao Paulo and Santos–Jundiahy lines and the Central Uruguay Railway; Charles Vignoles, for the Bahia–San Francisco line; and James Meadows Rendel, for the Pernambuco Railway in Brazil between Recife and Palmares. Rendel was succeeded on his death by Charles Hutton Gregory. The majority of the United Kingdom consultants were exactly that, and never visited the continent. Edwin Clark, of Britannia Bridge fame, was exceptional in not only visiting the continent, where he was engineer to various schemes, but actually being resident there during 1876–7. Clark was consultant for the Pernambuco State Government when early timber bridges were replaced by iron girders. He acted as consultant for the Buenos Aires and San Fernando Railway, and several lines in Uruguay, where he briefly lived.

Lines were built by agents of leading United Kingdom contractors, such as Brassey & Ogilvie who built Brazil's first line, the Maua Railway, between Rio and Petropolis (1852–6). Peto and Betts used the Rumball brothers, with their previous experience in Portugal, as agents on the Buenos Aires Great Southern Railway, built 1862–5. George Furness was contractor for the Pernambuco line, built 1855–62, and Edward Price was responsible for the first 38-mile stretch of the Dom Pedro II Railway in Brazil (1855–8) – Price had to remove a bridge on the line to secure payment for his work!

This British involvement owed much to British investment, with bankers like Rothschild's (Sao Paulo and Bahia), and Kennards (Pernambuco and Arica-Tacma in Peru) playing a prominent role. Inevitably British suppliers won contracts for locomotives and ironwork when iron rather than local timber or masonry could be afforded. As the century progressed, however, United States suppliers began to win contracts on the grounds of cost and reliability. By the time the Transandine Railway (Argentina to Chile) was built *c.* 1890 the British engineers responsible were using American suppliers.

It was an American, Henry Meiggs, who more than any individual dominated early Latin American railway construction. A larger than life character, like Pauling was to prove in Africa

PLATE 93 San Ramon Ravine, Santiago–Valparaiso Railway, *c.* 1860. 8.5 in x 6.5 in. Engineer: W. Lloyd; contractor: H. Meiggs; photographer: C.L. Rowsell

later in the century, Meiggs demonstrated the practicability of building railways in the Andes, and accumulated a fortune in the process. Meiggs had fled from California in 1854 to escape enormous debts (over $800,000). Shortly after his arrival in Chile in 1855 he won a contract for Maipo Bridge on the Santiago–Valparaiso Railway. Construction of the line had progressed very slowly. When William Lloyd, the United Kingdom engineer for the line, arrived in 1854 he had been assured the first thirty miles were near completion. In fact he discovered that little had been accomplished. Maughan, the resident engineer when construction began in 1853, had died shortly afterwards. There was no local experience in railway construction, and Lloyd discovered the station site in Valparaiso to be on 'a foundation of sand and filth of unspeakable noisomeness'.[1] The first three miles of the line 'crept along the base of the rocky cliffs of the coast, rendering [requiring] almost continuously massive sea-walls, and . . . a tunnel'.[2] The tunnel was the first completed on the Pacific Coast. By 1855, when this first section was opened, only eight miles had been completed. The railway had 'no mechanics, no engine driver, and only two engines . . . '.[3]

Despite Lloyd's efforts, by 1861 only 33 miles had been completed. Financial problems had halted construction in 1857 but Baring Brothers had stepped in to offer the Chilean Government a loan on the line. Unfortunately the local contractors Ovalle Brothers were unable to make a profit. At this stage Meiggs met the Minister of the Interior. He offered to complete the line in three years for 6 million pesos; for every month ahead of time he

PLATE 94 Manaos Bridge, *c.* 1880. 6 in x 4 in. Engineer/photographer: J. Pinkas

was to receive 510,000 pesos. Meiggs was awarded the contract and within fifteen days had four thousand men at work. The railway was completed in two years three days, Meiggs gaining a tremendous profit. The line cost almost £2,000,000, about £17,400 a mile. A variety of bridge types were used – timber, masonry, the largest being the Maglis Crossing with three 100 ft plate girders, and a 148 ft span box girder, supplied by the Canada Works, Birkenhead. Both Lloyd and Meiggs continued to make their careers in the continent, Meiggs eventually dying there. From Chile he went initially to survey railways in Bolivia (1863), and then to Peru.

Meiggs greatest contribution to railroad construction was his mastery of the Andes. The use of zig-zags to conquer precipitous mountains had been demonstrated by the British in the Indian Ghats in the 1850s, and subsequently in Australia. Meiggs employed them as never before or since. The Peruvian ambassador to Chile had realized his ability and persuaded his government to invite him to their country in 1868. Having just emerged from a period of civil war Peru could have done with time to recover some economic stability. Instead the new president, Jośe Balta, decided to plunge his country into a frenzy of railroad construction and national debt. Meiggs had no difficulty in getting his ear, and with the successful completion of each contract completed the economic ruin of the country. The first line Meiggs tackled was the line from Arequipa to Mollendo, involving a climb from sea level to 7,550 ft. Meiggs' tender was to complete the railway in three years for 12 million soles (*c.* £2.4 million), with a bonus or penalty of 2,000 soles a month. The railway was opened on 24 December 1870, six months ahead of schedule. A labour force of twelve thousand men had been recruited, the overwhelming majority being foreign, either from Chile, where Meiggs had established a good reputation, or China. More than two thousand men died on the job, but Meiggs' profit was handsome. The locomotives for the line were all American built, although British ironwork was preferred for the permanent way and bridges. Meiggs' success with this first contract brought further concessions in rapid succession. First came the extension to Puno, which Meiggs tendered for at £6 million compared with a competitor's estimate of £6.94 million, and then from Juliaca to Sicuani, for £5,192,800. Work on the Puno line began in 1870, with a predominately Bolivian workforce. Its 219 miles were not completed until 1876 due to Peru's increasing financial difficulties. Work on the Juliaca line began in 1872, but work had ground to a standstill by 1875, with 130 of 210 miles graded but no track laid. Balta had been assassinated in 1872 leaving a national debt of £60 million which guano could not pay off. The line was not resumed until 1877, the year of Meiggs' death. By that time Meiggs was desperate to find a solution to

Peru's and his own financial problems, and had won a concession to build a line from Oroya to the Cerro de Pascio mining district, hoping to open up the area's mineral wealth, a feat not accomplished until the end of the century.

Meiggs' greatest achievement was the Central Railway of Peru, from Callao via Lima to Oroya, and the highest railway in the world at the time. The original 1869 contract was for 27,600,000 soles, and the first 56 miles were built in nineteen months. Then financial problems led to the suspension of contracts, and it took six years for Meiggs to build the next 40 miles. At least ten thousand men died on the construction of the line, victims of Oroya fever and the hazards of construction. The line's summit was at 15,865 ft, and ten double and one single switches (zig-zags) were eventually required. The Verrugas Viaduct, 575 ft long and 252 ft high, was the third largest in the world at the time of its construction in 1871–3. It used Fink trusses supplied by the Baltimore Bridge Company. Other bridges were supplied by Eiffel. The line had to be cut out of sheer rock faces, and involved drilling sixty-five tunnels, including that under Mount Meiggs at 15,658 ft.

While Meiggs triumphed over the Andes, British engineers found less hazardous territories. British influence was greatest in Argentina where British capital and engineers developed an extensive railway system amounting to 24,000 miles by the 1920s, comparable to the route mileage in the United Kingdom itself. The first line was built between Buenos Aires and Floresta (1857). This was laid to the broad gauge (5 ft 3 in) with surplus materials from the Crimean War, and as a consequence two-thirds of the railway system followed on this gauge, with later light railways built to the 1 m gauge, and latterly a 2 ft gauge.

The Pampas, 'these immense distances in what appear a perfectly level plain, or ocean of land',[4] seemed ideally suited for railway construction. The complacent engineer might have supposed the greatest barrier to communication to be the herds of cattle and flocks of sheep who 'frightened by the engine, take it into their heads to follow one another in a stampede straight across the line in front of the train . . . '.[5] In fact these lines proved vulnerable to the effects of tropical flash floods. On 2–3 May 1877 a tremendous storm hit the country, with 6.5 in of rain falling on Buenos Aires in thirteen hours. Large sections of railway embankments and bridges were swept away and on the Compaca line alone 63,000 cubic m of earthwork had to be replaced.

In Brazil the problems of construction were more obvious. William Lloyd went there after working in Mexico, and commented, 'Living under canvas for two years in trackless woods . . . destitute sometimes not only of comforts, but even of wholesome foods, medicines, or a change of clothing, such things should

PLATE 95 Ponte da Cana Fistula, Baturite Railway, *c.* 1880. The railway was taken over by the Brazilian Government in 1878. The province of Ceara was stricken by drought, and the railway works were progressed to give relief to the population. 7.5 in x 5.5 in. Engineer and photographer: Briarque

entitle [engineers] to the best acknowledgement of all interested for services they so well performed'.[6] The Madeira–Mamore Railway, designed to circumvent rapids near the Brazil–Bolivian border, demonstrated the problems. An American engineer George End Church was appointed in 1868 by the Brazilian Government to report on the scheme. A British contractor was appointed in 1872 but resigned in 1873, defeated by the jungle. In 1877 P. and T. Collins, a Philadelphia firm, took up the project. During April 1878 the first rails were laid, and 220 miles of jungle had been surveyed, with 25 miles cleared and graded by the time the railway was abandoned in 1879 due to financial problems. Of the 940 men employed by Collins on the project, 200 died. Despite such debacles it is clear that it was not just the pursuit of money which persuaded engineers to tackle the tropics. 'It is hopeless to attempt any description of the luxuriance of a tropical flora, or of the intense wonder and enjoyment with which a naturalist first revels among its gorgeous charms.'[7] Thus was Edwin Clark smitten on his first arrival at Pernambuco. All the early concessions went to British interests, followed by American engineers in the 1860s. By the 1870s Brazilian engineers such as J. Pinkas had come to the fore, and the Brazilian Government was taking an increasingly active role in their management.

British engineers were responsible for a series of water supply and sewerage schemes in the second half of the century. In the case of the Rio de Janeiro main drainage, Brassey employed slave labour who proved hopeless for the task. Other schemes included Buenos Aires, Montevideo and Rosario de Sante Fe. In each case the water for supply was taken from the main river (Plate, Santa Lucia and Panama), and distributed by pumping station using steam engines supplied by British manufacturers. At Buenos Aires the original scheme designed by Coghlan was enlarged by J.F. Bateman as part of an overall scheme for the development of the port, water supply, sewerage and drainage of the town he was invited to draw up in 1870. The sanitary works were completed by Richard Clere Parsons, and took more than twenty years to finish, construction being held up from 1877–87. In the end the works were handed over by the city to a private company for completion.

Bateman's scheme for the port was not implemented. After many years' agitation Eduardo Malero, a local businessman, got the approval of Congress in 1882 for a docks scheme. Baring Brothers recommended Sir John Hawkshaw as a suitable engineer and his firm drew up the plans. On Hawkshaw's recommendation, T.A. Walker was appointed contractor, with Armstrong's supplying the hydraulic works. Work began in 1887, and was not completed until 1898. The chief port on the Pacific coast, Valparaiso, in Chile, was also improved by British engineers. Prior to 1883 cargo had to be transferred from ship to shore in launches. In that year a mole was completed, founded on wrought-iron cylinders, 105 ft long, and served by hydraulic cranes. Interestingly, the pneumatic caissons used for the foundations were installed by Willoughby Rochester Hughes, son of John Hughes, who had been responsible for the first use of the method in bridge foundations at Rochester Bridge.

The crossing of the isthmus encapsulated all the problems of civil engineering in the continent. It was alternatively dream and nightmare, but still inspired the major civil engineering project of the epoch. The advantages of a sea canal through Central America had been realized almost as soon as the Spaniards arrived in the area in the sixteenth century. The first half of the nineteenth century saw a variety of proposals, which concentrated on the main locations: Nicaragua, Tehuantepec (Mexico), and Darien (Panama). These were generally based on an ignorance of the geology and geography of the area, and seemingly authoritative words misled politicians and engineers for generations. The first demonstration of the practical problems involved was provided by the California Goldrush of 1849. With the alternatives of a trek across the United States, or a ship around the Horn, many took the chance of a scramble across the Isthmus of Panama with a considerable saving in time – if you survived the jungle and disease. Railway speculators realized that there was a 'killing to be made', and in 1850 an American company got the concession from the Colombian (then New Grenada) Government. It took five years to build rather than the original estimate of two. The cost in life was immense – between 6,000 and 12,000 died (no records were kept of the non-white workforce) and the problems of disease, particularly malaria and yellow fever, and terrain were revealed. The railway proved immensely profitable, and it demonstrated there was a route across the isthmus at Culebra at a height of only 275 ft above sea level, which had been unknown before. In nearby Nicaragua another crossing was built, making use of steamers on the rivers and lakes, and it was discovered by the engineer Orville Childs that a lower crossing point (153 ft) existed than at Panama. Further north in Mexico the Tehuantepec Railway was built, but was never as popular as its competitors. For the next twenty years pressure for a canal increased, and engineers from the United States came on increasingly frequent surveying parties to investigate the alternatives. Accompanied by professional photographers such as Timothy O'Sullivan and military photographers like Captain H.A. Bartlett, they revealed the inadequacy of existing information, and the scale of the problem.

Despite the American effort, it was the efforts of a Frenchman in his late sixties, with no engineering training, which finally got a scheme off the ground – Ferdinand de Lesseps. Inspired by the success of Suez, completed in 1869, and with a desire to restore French pride so humbled in the Franco–Prussian war, de Lesseps became associated with a syndicate who managed to gain a concession for the canal from Colombia. The scheme was based on very inadequate surveys of the area, and, unfortunately, de Lesseps became obsessed with the idea that a sea level canal could be built. So impressed had he been with the problems overcome at Suez he seems to have believed engineering progress could solve anything. In 1879 an international congress was held in Paris to discuss the alternative routes, and the practicalities of construction. By force of personality de Lesseps got his obsession – the sea level crossing at Panama, accepted. He then went on a publicity tour, which in France in particular was spectacularly successful in gaining support for the scheme. Unfortunately it was undercapitalized from the start, and much money was squandered before work actually began. The purchase of the railway concession further exhausted the resources. While financial problems were inevitable some attempt was made to foresee the health problems, and hospital accommodation was erected. Unfortunately the association between malaria, yellow fever and mosquitos was only beginning to be suspected, and the hospitals failed to take any precautions against the insect. The result was human tragedy, which decimated the ranks of the young French engineers who volunteered for the project. The first chief French engineer, Gaston Blanchet, died within a year, the second, Jules Dingler, lost all his family. Estimates of the death rate varies between 20 per cent and 50 per cent, with up to forty workers dying a day.

With an inbuilt financial problem, and the ravages of disease making continuity of work well nigh impossible the engineering problems almost appear insignificant: but de Lesseps' obsession

PLATE 96 Culebra Cut, Panama Canal, under construction, November 1888

with a sea level canal had made the scheme virtually impossible. The Culebra cut was through an extremely unstable geological formation, prone to mud slides, which excavation work only aggravated. Rather than removing spoil the French tried to terrace it, and the result was more mud slides. The excavation work was made more treacherous by the torrential rains – up to 6 in of rain in a day was not uncommon – and the consequent flooding of the rivers, most notably the Chagres which was capable of regularly rising over 10 ft in twenty-four hours. There had been no plan to deal with this until Dingler decided to try and dam it with the largest earth dam in the world.

Excavation of the canal began in 1882, with the workforce rising to over twenty thousand in 1884. By that time massive steam dredgers were at work, largely provided by American contractors. By the following year financial problems, the scale of the technical problems, and the human tragedy were beginning to have an impact. With the resignation of Dingler and his very brief successor, the 27-year-old Philippe Bunau Varilla became chief engineer. He could see the problems of a sea level canal, and began to advocate a lock canal as a temporary expedient – to save de Lesseps' face. He took over responsibility, using explosives to shatter the rock so it could be excavated by dredgers. By 1887 de Lesseps had come to accept the lock proposal, and Eiffel was brought in as contractor for the locks. There was increasing talk of financial impropriety, and disaster finally overtook the company in February 1889, resulting in Eiffel and de Lesseps' son Charles

PLATE 97 Lock 4, Panama Canal, 7 November 1888, about eight and a half months after the start of work. Engineer: P. Bunau Varilla; contractor: G. Eiffel

being sentenced to prison for their involvement in what proved to be extremely dubious financial schemes to keep the canal afloat.

The French Panama effort can hardly be seen as a success for civil engineers, but despite the morass into which the scheme sank, engineering achievements were considerable. Over 19 million cubic yd of material were excavated at Culebra and overall 50 million (73 million by 1903) along the canal length. A vast amount of geological and hydrological information was gathered, and the practicability of the scheme had been demonstrated in an engineering sense if not in terms of its finance or its price in human life. If it was the greatest civil engineering failure of the nineteenth century it also demonstrated how far engineering had advanced in fifty years. It had cost 1.435 million Francs – more than any other undertaking hitherto – but much had been learnt to facilitate the ultimate triumph of the American-led project in 1914.

NOTES

1. W. Lloyd, *A Railway Pioneer*, 1900, p. 66.
2. W. Lloyd, op. cit., pp. 66–7.
3. W. Lloyd, op. cit., p. 67.
4. E. Clark, *A Visit to South America*, 1878, p. 142.
5. E. Clark, op. cit., pp. 148–9.
6. W. Lloyd, op. cit., p. 172.
7. E. Clark, op. cit., p. 72.

CHAPTER FOURTEEN

From Cape to Cairo

. . . when the engineer has completed his task something will still remain beyond the range of mechanics. Africa will remain the unique, the indefinable, the most baffling of the continents.

Jan Smuts, 26 May 1922, from The Story of the Cape to Cairo Railway, *ed. L. Weinthall.*

Africa, the scene of the great engineering achievements of ancient Egypt, was the site of one of the engineering wonders of the nineteenth century: the Suez Canal. Beyond it Africa provided work for British and French engineers and suppliers, but, for the British at least, on a more modest scale than in other continents. In the early nineteenth century the interior of Africa was unknown to Europeans. The North African coast was part of the Mediterranean world and as such had close historical links with Europe. Elsewhere, since the fifteenth century led initially by the Portuguese, Europeans had established a series of trading posts. Gradually the Dutch and French established similar posts. The Dutch Cape settlement originated as a revictualling station for their East India trade. British involvement was at first largely confined to West Africa – the Gold Coast (Ghana), Sierra Leone and Gambia. Very little of this pre-colonial development penetrated inland.

In 1795–6 Mungo Park had attempted to remedy the lack of knowledge of Africa's interior, and establish the course of the Niger, but he had to turn back because of hostility from the Moslem population. In 1805 he tried again and all his party were wiped out by natives. Despite such setback, by the 1830s clearer spheres of influence were developing. The British in their anti-slavery push became dominant in West Africa. The French, after a brief foray into Egypt under Napoleon, had established themselves on the Algerian coast, and between 1835 and 1840 the Boers, anxious to escape British influence, began to settle the High Veld beyond the Orange River. In the 1840s further military action increased the French presence in Algeria, and extended

British South Africa to include Natal. It was not, however, until the 1880s that the scramble for Africa began in earnest, a process that by 1914 meant that all Africa except Abyssinia and Liberia was under European influence, largely British and French.

Given the limited nature of European influence and settlement in Africa for much of the nineteenth century, it is hardly surprising that European civil engineers had few opportunities to practice their skills. This was not for lack of potential work. Internal communications were primitive to say the least. In 1849 the wife of a colonial official, Elizabeth Melville, wrote, of Sierra Leone, 'There are no such things as carts, waggons or even hand barrows in the place',[1] after more than half a century of British occupation. Thirty years later C.O. Burge discovered that distance in South Africa was measured in hours rather than miles, so poor were internal communication.

The earliest attempt of civil engineering of any significance was a breakwater at Table Bay in 1748. Although funds were raised, very little was achieved, and nearly a century later (1829) all that existed to service the considerable amount of shipping was a decayed wharf, with the result that much shipping suffered storm damage.

PLATE 98 Point railway station, Port Natal, *c.* 1860. Engineer: A. Robinson

In 1828 the earliest suggestions for a railway in Africa came from the Cape Town Chamber of Commerce. Nothing came of this proposal or the 1845 Cape of Good Hope Western Railway, and it was not until 1854 that a proposal, that of the Cape Town Railway and Dock Company, got off the ground. With John Scott Tucker, who had worked with I. K. Brunel and Sir John Rennie, as consultant in South Africa, Sir Charles Fox as United Kingdom consultant, and William George Brounger as resident engineer, it had a team of great ability and experience. Progress was, however, painfully slow: work did not begin until 1859, and Wellington, the intended terminus, was not reached until 4 November 1863. The labour force, like the material, had to be imported from the United Kingdom, a pattern followed for most subsequent development until Indian labour was substituted for British in the later schemes.

Progress on the Cape line was so slow that it was not the first line to be opened in southern Africa. That honour went to the line between Durban and Port Natal, opened on 26 June 1860. Both these lines were very short, and the major early railway development in Africa was taking place at the other end of the continent.

Egypt, nominally still part of the Ottoman Empire, but with considerable independence under the rule of Mohammed Ali and his successors, came under increasing pressure from France and Britain to grant concessions. The British were particularly interested in potential savings in communication time with India if transport could be improved between the Mediterranean and Red seas. In 1834 track was laid for a line for the Indian mail, between Alexandria and Suez, but the scheme was abandoned on the death of R.H. Galloway, engineer to Mohammed Ali. In 1845 new docks were completed at Alexandria, increasing British pressure for a rail link. Finally on 12 July 1851 Robert Stephenson was appointed engineer for a line from Alexandria to Suez via Cairo. The resident engineer on the scheme was Michael Andrew Borthwick, and the contractor Edward Price. The most interesting features of this line were the tubular bridges modelled on the Britannia Bridge. Ironwork was supplied by Grissells and the bridges were supported on iron caissons. Railway construction proceeded apace in Egypt, with 941 miles completed by 1882, a large amount under Ismail, the most vigorous of Mohammed Ali's descendants, who saw 537 miles completed between 1863 and 1869, much by French companies.

The French were even more active in Algeria. Initially the Emperor Napoleon III consulted Sir John Fowler and Sir Morton Peto about a railway network for the colony in 1857, and they both visited Algeria. Not surprisingly the work was taken up by French engineers, and many of the lines were laid by the military with convict labour, giving very real support to French colonial expansion in the area. The first line was built by the military, 1858–62, as the first stage in the link between Algiers and Oran. This line was taken over in 1863 by the Paris–Lyon–Mediterranean Railway Company. Subsequently contracts on three lines were awarded to Brassey Peto and Company, but this was exceptional. By the early 1880s over 1,000 miles of railway had been laid, the most extensive system in Africa.

In South Africa railway development remained slow. Despite many proposals, only 154 miles of railway had been built as late as 1875. Then with the discovery of diamonds near the Vaad River in 1867, the position changed dramatically. By 1872 there were fifty thousand people in the area, with the Kimberley mine being discovered in 1871. The goldfields of the Witwatersrand followed in 1886, transforming the economic circumstances of Transvaal. To deal with this mineral wealth a railway rush began from the coast and the Cape Government took over existing lines in 1873, drawing up plans for an extensive network. By 1885 there were 1,654 miles of railway in the Cape, with a direct link between Cape Town and Kimberley. The government lines were built to a 3 ft 6 in gauge, which colonial authorities felt would be the most economical solution for the mountainous terrain, and the limited financial resources made available. Railways were also being built from Durban to the interior. The bulk of the lines were the work of government engineers under William Brounger, with Sir Charles Hutton Gregory as United Kingdom consultant. Work was carried out by contractors with established firms like Wythes and Jackson (Durban, Pietermaritzburg) and Westwood Baillie (ironwork contractors) getting contracts. For ironwork suppliers the lines proved unusually profitable as even short-span culverts were bridged in iron due to lack of skilled masonry workers. Even when President Kruger attempted to get a railway built from Laurenco Marques to the Transvaal, to avoid dependence on British-controlled lines, the first section from Delagoa Bay to the border was built by Sir Thomas Tancred (1887). There was a high human cost as the first 40 of the 55 miles were mosquito-infested swamps. Eventually in the 1890s the Portuguese authorities took the line over, and the link to the Transvaal was completed.

The name most associated with South African railway development is George Pauling. Although he only came to the fore in the years of the scramble for Africa, when he built much of the railway network to support British colonial expansion, he had been involved in railway construction since 1869 when he briefly worked on the Metropolitan District Railway. In the early 1870s he gained valuable site experience working for the railway contractors Joseph and Ralph Firbank.

In November 1875, at the age of twenty, he set sail with his brother Henry for Cape Colony, to join his father who had been

PLATES 99 and 100 Kimberley mines, *c.* 1883. 14 in x 11.5 in

PLATE 101 Colesberg Bridge, Cape Government Railways. One of a series of photographs taken by the ironwork contractors of various of their projects in the 1860s. Rival firms such as Kennards and Handyside's were using similar photographs as the basis for illustrating books about their products about the same time. Surviving American examples date from the 1870s. Engineers: Sir George Berkley, William George Brounger; ironwork construction and photography: Westwood Baillie & Company

appointed an engineer for the Cape Government Railways. Pauling was employed to supervise a tunnel near Grahamstown. With experience of tunnel construction at Helm, Dewsbury, and in London, Pauling saw that more money could be made as contractor than government engineer. He took up several contracts on the line, intended to run from Grahamstown to Port Elizabeth, and made about £15,000 before the pace of railway work slackened. He then became involved in a variety of business ventures, including the ownership of the Majestic Hotel. He was, however, bitten by the contracting bug, and before long he managed to raise the capital for a railway, the Kowie Railway, from Grahamstown to the sea at Port Alfred. To do this he had photographs taken of Port Alfred and the Kowie river to entice investors, and then set sail for England. With the help of Ralph Firbank, Pauling was able to raise the capital and a guarantee of interest from the Government. The chief engineering feature of the line was a 300 ft-span cantilever bridge designed by Max am Ende at Blaankrantz. The railway was built by Firbank and Pauling and opened

PLATE 102 15-ton block-setting machine for Port Alfred Harbour, 1877. Engineer: Sir John Coode; supplier: Stothert & Pitt; photography: Stothert & Pitt

in 1884. At more or less the same time the firm won the contract for a 90-mile stretch of line from Sterkstrom to Aliwal North. The success of these schemes led to the contract for the Orange River to Kimberley railway, where rapidity of construction was of the essence. The 75 miles were built in nine months. Despite this the contract bankrupted Pauling. Because of the speed with which the contract was drawn up many clauses were very vague, and the cost of the work on Kimberley station proved beyond Pauling's credit. With three contracts on the go more or less simultaneously Pauling was travelling 2–3,000 miles a month and working from dawn until eleven o'clock at night, generally sleeping in carts or on the railway.

Pauling then turned to the goldfields before returning to England and dabbling in more railway schemes. It was not until 1889 that he returned to South Africa and railway contracting, initially in partnership with James Butler as James Butler and Company on the 'Rand Tram' from Johannesburg to Boksburg. This coincided with a major increase in railway work in Africa, and proved the foundation of a continuous period of successful contracting by Pauling, which was eventually to extend worldwide.

If Pauling was to prove the great name in civil engineering in Africa, the great project was undoubtedly the Suez Canal. The earliest hydraulic works in Egypt, aside from the Alexandria Docks, were two barrages across the Nile at Damietta and Rosetta. Designed by a French engineer, Mougel, work began in 1843 and was not completed until 1861. The barrages were only partially successful and had to be rebuilt in the 1890s. Further schemes were

PLATE 103 Excavation in the dry Suez Canal at 88 km, *c.* 1869. Engineer: Voisin Bey; contractor: Borel & Lavalley; photographer: Kozlouski

discussed, including an ambitious Sweet Water canal scheme devised by John Fowler when taking a convalescent rest in Egypt.

As a result of the world shortage of cotton during the American Civil War, Egypt, as an alternative supplier, was able to raise much capital, particularly in the French markets, to finance further railway and irrigation projects, but the Suez scheme was the most spectacular. Napoleon had dreamt of a canal across the Suez Isthmus as an imperial work to match the Pharaohs' and in the 1820s and '30s the British developed a route for steamer communications with India via the Mediterranean and Red Sea using an overland link across Egypt. In the 1830s Ferdinand de Lesseps was French Consul in Egypt, and got to know Prince Said. After De Lesseps' retirement from the foreign service Prince Said came to power in Egypt in 1854. De Lesseps, although no engineer, was inspired by the Napoleonic dream, and persuaded Said to sanction plans for a canal. Although the design was approved by an international commission including United Kingdom consultants it was the work of French engineers led by Voisin Bey, and French contracting firms. With a labour force of twenty thousand men the canal was completed in ten years and opened on 17 February 1869.

The canal was 164 km long and initially 8 m deep and 22 m wide at the bottom. Much of the work was carried out using steam dredgers and elevators, modelled on Dutch examples, by the French contractors Borel and Lavalley. Up to sixty dredgers were used at a time, shifting a staggering 2 million cubic m of silt a month. The workforce was initially largely forced Egyptian labour, but from May 1864 this was replaced by a mixed force of Europeans, Africans and Middle Eastern workers. The canal inspired a range of ship canal projects across the world in the last quarter of the nineteenth century. With the British purchase of Said's shareholding in 1874, it also increased British influence in the area, paving the way for a series of British-designed public works projects in the final decade of the nineteenth century and in the early twentieth century, notably the Aswan dams and Cairo's main drainage scheme.

The Suez Canal was the most ambitious civil engineering scheme in Africa prior to Rhodes' dream of the Cape to Cairo Railway. Other measures were taken to improve sea communications with Africa. As was found in India these schemes met with varying success, partly due to imperfect understanding of sea and coastline processes. Problems were undoubtedly formidable, John Scott Russell speaking of 'solid columns of water, sometimes as high as 30 ft, rolling in with an enormous progressive motion' at the Cape. At Port Elizabeth in Algoa Bay, which had been the busiest of the South African ports, early improvement works were disastrous. In 1856 a 1,700 ft-long breakwater was commenced to protect the harbour from the south-east. Following its completion in 1865 serious silting ensued, destroying the harbour by 1869. Sir John Coode was consulted and recommended opening out the existing breakwater and further extending it. Progress was slow, and in 1876 Sir John Hawkshaw and James Brunlees agreed to a new scheme with a new breakwater 3,000 ft out from the coast, enclosing a much larger harbour with docks. These works took more than ten years to complete.

At Port Natal harbour works were scarcely more successful. Following the seizure of Natal by the British in 1842–3 John Milne, a pupil of the Rennies, arrived in 1849. He identified problems of longshore drift and a bar at the port entrance. He hoped to use piers to increase tidal scour at the harbour entrance. By 1857 little had been achieved and a revised scheme was drawn up by James Vetch, a Royal engineer, and in 1859 James Abernethy was appointed engineer-in-chief. He drew up contract documents, and United Kingdom contractor Thomas Jackson was the successful tenderer. None of these individuals (Vetch, Abernethy or Jackson) had visited the port. The design was prepared in ignorance of the harbour and the contractor had no idea of local costs. After two years' work in September 1863 it was clear the contractors' estimates were hopeless and in November Abernethy recommended taking the contract for stonework away from the contrac-

PLATE 104 Table Bay Dry Dock excavation, 1877. Engineer: Sir John Coode

tor and completing this work by direct labour. The Government referred the question to two Natal Government engineers. In August 1864, before their recommendations could be acted on, Jackson threw up the contract. It was clear that the work carried out so far was inadequate for the purpose, with ironwork and timber already showing signs of decay. Peter Paterson, a government engineer, took over the works while a decision was made on what to do. In 1867 Sir John Coode was appointed consultant, and he sent an assistant, Neate, to Durban to gather information. Unfortunately Neate's report included a misguided belief in a rock reef at the harbour entrance. Nothing was achieved, despite further reports by Coode, until after the Zulu War in 1879.

In 1881 the Natal Harbour Board was created, with Edward Innes as engineer. Like his predecessor, Innes believed in the need for piers to enhance tidal scour, but, crucially, he ordered a dredger, which revealed that it was possible to keep the silt at bay without reliance on scour. Innes died at the age of thirty-five and in 1888 his assistant, and temporary successor, Charles Croft, demonstrated there was no rock reef to be cleared, and ordered a further dredger. Because of his age (he was only thirty-one in 1887) Crofts was appointed assistant to a new chief engineer, Methven. Methven and Crofts continued work on the piers as well as dredging, with the result that by the early twentieth century Durban had an adequate harbour at long last.

Important harbour works were also undertaken in North Africa. At Algiers French engineers, led by Poirel, were responsible for the first use of concrete blockwork, and the most extensive use of mass concrete since Roman times, when they rebuilt the breakwater between 1833 and 1840. Nearby Alexandria was the leading Mediterranean port after Marseilles and Geneva. After the initial flurry of activity under Mohammed Ali, relatively little was done until under Ismail Pasha a scheme was adopted to the designs of the French engineer Linant de Bellefonds, Minister of Public Works, in 1869. A breakwater was built 1870–3, together with a coaling jetty and additional quays. Growth in trade led to further work at the end of the century. At Table Bay and Cape Town more success was achieved. The idea of a breakwater at Cape Town has already been referred to. Proposals continued through the 1850s, but it was not until 1860 that work began on Sir John Coode's scheme. This involved a 3,600 ft rubble breakwater and two basins. Although extensions were proposed in the 1880s nothing was done until the 1890s. Perhaps of greater interest is the Cape's cast-iron lighthouse, one of several prefabricated in England and shipped to the colonies in the mid-nineteenth century. The Cape Point Lighthouse was designed by Alexander Gordon and manufactured by the Victoria Foundry at Greenwich. Gordon established quite a reputation for this rather unusual nineteenth-century British export, designing his first such lighthouse (Morant Point) in 1841.

The objective of this lighthouse, as with many other examples of African engineering, was to provide a cheap solution to an engineering problem. Before the discovery of mineral wealth and the territorial scramble at the end of the century, relatively little had been achieved. Port plans were governed by limited money as was the narrow gauge of much of the railways. In Egypt grandiose schemes reflected the ambitions of the local rulers, and proximity of financial backers, but even here ambition exceeded funds. With the notable exception of Suez, in truth there had been little for the engineering photographer to record.

NOTE

1. E.H. Melville, *A Residence at Sierre Leone*, London: Cass, 1968.

Sources and Select Bibliography

ARCHIVAL SOURCES

Great civil engineering works are affairs of State. It is almost inevitable, therefore, that the study of the history of civil engineering will involve the use of State records' repositories. While the main specialist civil engineering archives in the United Kingdom are those of the Institution of Civil Engineers and the Science Museum, the Public Records Office has the largest collection of original material. This includes material relating to the old railway and canal companies arising from nationalization in addition to information on central government's role. The Scottish Records Office and the National Library of Wales perform similar functions for Scotland and Wales. Elsewhere the value and comprehensiveness of national archives will depend on local circumstances and the ravages of war. Generally speaking, central governments played a more prominent role in infrastructure development outside Great Britain. In some countries this was due to the relative backwardness of capital formation, and elsewhere to a more centralized administrative structure. Tracing official records is complicated by the political changes of the twentieth century. In Europe there were major boundary changes following the two World Wars. Poland, for example, was partitioned between the Russian, Prussian and Austro-Hungarian empires in the nineteenth century making its history particularly complicated. The creation of nation states out of the Habsburg Empire also makes it difficult to trace records. Not only was there a varying amount of local administrative control in the Habsburg period, but after the creation of the dual monarchy following the 1848 revolution, parts of modern countries like Czechoslovakia were administratively split between Vienna and Budapest.

Prior to 1914 much of the globe formed part of European empires, and it is to Europe rather than local resources that one must often turn for original records. Even where political independence was achieved, notably in Latin America, economic independence was rare. Much work was carried out by foreign engineers for foreign companies. Twentieth-century nationalization may mean that original records have been lost.

Generally speaking, civil engineering records can be divided into two groups, those that relate to existing civil engineering works or concerns, and those that relate to historic structures or defunct concerns. It is possible that while a work survives its owner will have relevant records. Once a structure has disappeared survival of records is less likely unless it was the work of a well-known engineer whose papers may have been archived independently. War, shortage of space, changes of ownership and other ravages of time have all conspired against survival, and often archaeological evidence is all that remains.

Local record offices may provide most help in these circumstances. Local authorities, municipal and provincial governments, often have a regulating role even when direct ownership is not involved. In addition they attract the records of local firms and individuals. In the United Kingdom they generally contain information on local ports, roads, bridge and drainage works, and records of local firms. They are particularly important sources of information on civil engineering works carried out before the nineteenth century, when there are very few published sources.

National libraries are the obvious sources for published information. Although the British Library does not aim to collect civil engineering archives the scale of its collection of State papers, maps, and holdings of published material make it a major international resource. Because of political changes it may be more comprehensive than many national libraries and collections.

The personal papers of engineers, and company records are probably the resource most underused by historians. This is a result of difficulties in tracing descendants whether corporate or individual. Not every effort of such a search will be rewarded, but recent accessions to the archives of the Institution of Civil Engineers indicate there is much of historical importance still in private hands.

The chief strength of the Institution of Civil Engineers' collection is its information on the history of the profession. ICE has records relating to the Institution's own development. The leading professional engineering institution of the century, it was a model for such institutions worldwide. In addition they have the records of the Smeatonian Society of Engineers, and the Institution of Municipal Engineers. In recent years the Institution's Archives Panel has been striving to develop a representative collection of civil engineering material for the period.

Information on the key figures of the period is widely scattered. The largest collection of Brunel material is at Bristol University. Locke's career has to be traced through various record offices, although Bradford have adopted him as their own. ICE, the Institution of Mechanical Engineers, the Science Museum and Newcastle all have material on the Stephensons. George Parker Bidder's papers, more logically, are at the Science Museum. The Institution of Civil Engineers has recently acquired a largely intact collection of the papers of William Mackenzie, a leading railway contractor of the first half of the nineteenth century and partner of Thomas Brassey, as well as some relating to Thomas Townshend, another contemporary. Information on Kirkaldy can be found at the Kirkaldy Testing Museum, Southwark.

CHAPTER ONE

Andrew, J.H., 'The copying of engineering drawings and documents', Newcomen Society, *Transactions*, 1981–2, pp. 1–13.

Train Spotting: images of the railways in art, Castle Museum, Nottingham, 1985.

Eder, J.M., *The history of photography*, New York: Dover, 1978.

Gernsheim, H. and A., *The history of photography*, Oxford: Univeristy Press, 1955; third edition, 2 volumes, Thames and Hudson (in progress).

Gernsheim, H., *Incunabula of British photographic literature: a bibliography of photographic literature 1839–1875*, London: Scolar Press, 1984.

Lecuyer, R., *Historie de la photographie*, New York: Arno Press, 1979.

Lemagny, J-C. and Rouille, A., *A history of photography*, Cambridge: University Press, 1987.

Newhall, B., *The history of photography from 1839 to the present*, revised edition, London: Secker and Warburg, 1982.

Photographers' Gallery, *British industrial photography 1843–1986*, London: The Gallery, 1986. Especially Pugh, F., 'Industry and the photographer 1843–1914', pp. 8–36.

CHAPTER TWO

Armytage, W.H.G., *A social history of engineering*, London: Faber and Faber, 1961.

Biswas, A.K., *History of hydrology*, Amsterdam: North Holland, 1972.

Boucher, C.T.G., *John Rennie, 1761–1821*, Manchester: University Press, 1963.

Boucher, C.T.G., *James Brindley, engineer*, Norwich: Gosse, 1968.

Buchanan, R.A., *The engineers: a history of the engineering profession in Britain 1750–1914*, London: Jessica Kingsley, 1989.

Coulton, J.J., *Greek architects at work*, London: P. Elek, 1977.

Darby, H.C., *The draining of the fens*, second edition, Cambridge: University Press, 1956.

Emmerson, G.S., *Engineering education: a social history*, Newton Abbot: David and Charles, 1973.

Fitchen, John, *The construction of gothic cathedrals*, Chicago: University Press, 1961.

Fitchen, John, *Building construction before mechanization*, Cambridge, Mass.: MIT, 1986.

Gibb, A., *The story of Telford*, Edinburgh: Alexander Maclehouse, 1935.

Hadfield, C., *British canals*, seventh edition, Newton Abbot: David and Charles, 1985.

Heyman, J., *Coulomb's memoir on statics*, Cambridge: University Press, 1972.

Jansen, D., *Civil engineering around 1700*, Copenhagen: DTP, 1971.

Kerisel, J., *The history of geotechnical engineering up until 1700*, 11th International Conference on Soil Mechanics and Foundation Engineering, 1985, Golden Jubilee volume, pp. 3–94.

Kurrer, K.E., *Die Baustatik in Frankreich und Deutschland in frühen 19 Jahrhundert*, Berlin: TG, 1986–7.

Kurrer, K.E., *Das Verhältniss von Bautechnik und Stalik*, Berlin: Ernst, (Bautechnik) 1985.

Landes, D.J., *The unbound Prometheus*, Cambridge: University Press, 1969.

Penfold, A., ed., *Thomas Telford, engineer*, London: Thomas Telford Limited, 1980.

Picon, A., *Architectes et ingenieurs au siècle des luminaries*, Marseille: Editions Parentheses, 1988.

Rolt, L.T.C., *Thomas Telford*, London: Longman, 1958.

Rouse, H. and Ince, S., *History of hydraulics*, Iowa: Institute of Hydraulic Research, 1957.

Ruddock, E., *Arch bridges and their builders 1735–1835*, Cambridge: University Press, 1979.

Rumen de Armas, A., *Ciencia y tecnologia en la España Ilustrada*, Madrid: Turner, 1980.

Singer, C. and others, eds., *A history of technology*, Oxford: Clarendon, 1958.

Skempton, A.W., ed., *John Smeaton, FRS*, London: Thomas Telford Limited, 1982.

Skempton, A.W., 'The engineering works of John Grundy', *Lincolnshire History and Archaeology*, volume 19, 1984, pp. 65–82.

Skempton, A.W. and Hadfield, C., *William Jessop, engineer*, London: David and Charles.

Smith, N.A.F., *A heritage of Spanish dams*, Madrid: Spanish National Committee on Large Dams, 1970.

Straub, H., *A history of civil engineering*, London: L. Hill, 1960.

Summers, D., *The Great Level*, Newton Abbot: David and Charles, 1976.
Tann, J., *The selected papers of Boulton and Watt, volume 1*, London: Diploma Press, 1981.
Timoshenko, S.P., *History of strength of materials*, New York: McGraw-Hill, 1953.
Walker, R.J.B., *Old Westminster Bridge*, Newton Abbot: David and Charles, 1979.
Watson, J.G., *The Smeatonians*, London: Thomas Telford Limited, 1989.
Weiss, J.H., *The making of technological man*, Cambridge, Mass.: MIT, 1983.
Wright, N.R., *John Grundy of Spalding, engineer*, Lincoln: Lincolnshire County Council, 1983.

CONTEMPORARY SOURCES

Serials

Academie [Royale] des Sciences, Paris.
Histoire memoires, 1666–.
Annales des arts et manufacturers, 1800–15.
Gentleman's magazine, 1731–1922.
Mechanics magazine, 1823–1872.
Philosophical magazine, 1798–.
Recueil polytechnique des ponts et chaussées, 1804–7.
Repertory of arts and manufactures, 1794–1825; *patent invention* 1825–63.
Royal Society, Philosophical transactions, 1665–
Sammlung von Aufsatzen und Nachrichten, die Baukunst betreffend, 1797–1800.

Books

Agricola, G., *De Re metallica*, Basle, 1556, reprinted London: *Mining magazine*, 1912.
Andreossy, F., *Historie du Canal du Midi*, first and second editions, Paris: 1799, 1804.
Barlow, P., 'An essay on the strength and stress of timber', London: J. Taylor, 1817.
Belidor, B.F., *La Science des ingenieurs*, Paris: Jombert, 1729.
Belidor, B.F., *Architecture hydraulique*, 4 volumes, Paris: Jombert, 1737.
Bernouilli, D., *Hydrodynamica*, Argentoratie: J. Reinhold, 1738.
Dugdale, Sir W., *The history of embanking and draining of rivers, fens and marshes*, second edition, London: Owen, 1772.
Eytelwein, J.A., *Handbuch der Mechanik fester Körper und der Hydraulik*, Berlin: 1801.
Gautier, H., *Traité des ponts*, Paris: A. Cailleau, 1716.
Gerstner, F.J.R., *Handbuch der Mechanik*, 3 volumes, Prague: Spurry, 1832–4.
Gilly, D. and Eytelwein, J.A., *Praktische Anweisung zur Wasserbaukunst*, Berlin: Realschulbechandlung, 1805–18.
Girard, P.S., *Traité de la resistance des solides . . .*, Paris: Didot, 1798.
Jousse, M., *Le Théatre de l'art de charpentier*, Paris: La Flèche, 1627.
McAdam, J.L., *Remarks on the present system of road making*, various editions, London: Longman, 1821, etc.
Mayneil, H., *Traité experimental, analytique et pratique de la poussée des terres et des murs de revêtement*, Paris: Colas, 1808.
Perronet, J.R., *Description des projets et de construction des ponts de Neuilly, de Nantes, d'Orléans et autres*, Paris, 1782–9.
Ramelli, A., *Le Diverse et artificiose machine*, Paris, 1588.
Robison, John, *A system of mechanical philosophy*, 4 volumes, Edinburgh: J. Murray, 1822.
Rondelet, J., *Traité théorique et pratique de l'art de bâtir*, Paris, 1805–10.
Smeaton, J., *A narrative of the building and a description of the construction of the Eddystone lighthouse*, London, 1791.
Smeaton, J., *Reports*, 4 volumes, London: Longman, 1798, 1812.
Smiles, S., *Lives of the engineers*, various editions, London: Murray, 1874, etc.
Switzer, S., *An introduction to a general system of hydrostaticks*, 2 volumes, London, 1729.
Todhunter, I. and Pearson, K., *A history of the theory of elasticity*, 2 volumes in 3, Cambridge: University Press, 1886–93.
Vauban, S. Le P., *De l'attacque et de la défense places fortes*, La Hague, 1737.
Vermuyden, Sir Cornelius, *A Discourse touching the dredging of the Great Fens . . .*, London: T. Fawcett, 1642.
Wells, S., *History of the great level of the fens*, 2 volumes and map, London: S. Wells, 1830.
Woltman, R., *Beytrage zur hydraulischen Architectur*, 4 volumes in 2, Gottingen: J.C. Dietrich, 1791.
Zeising, H., *Theatri machinarum*, I-6 Theil, Leipzig: Henning Grossen, *c.* 1613–15.

CHAPTER THREE

Addis, W., *Structural engineering: the nature of theory and design*, Chichester: Ellis Horwood, 1990.
Beckett, D., *Brunel's Britain*, Newton Abbot: David and Charles, 1980.
Benvenuto, E., *An introduction to the history of structural mechanics*, 2 volumes, New York: Springer, 1991.
Booth, L.G. and others, 'Thomas Tredgold', 5 parts, Newcomen Society, *Transactions*, volume 51, 1979, pp. 57–94
Brooke, D., *The railway navvy*, Newton Abbot: David and Charles, 1983.
Brown, J.M., 'W.B. Wilkinson (1819–1902) and his place in the history of reinforced concrete', Newcomen Society, *Transactions*, volume 39, 1966–7, p. 129–42.
Charlton, T.M., *A history of the theory of structures in the nineteenth century*, Cambridge: University Press, 1982.
Coleman, T., *The railway navvies*, London: Hutchinson, 1965.
Dickinson, H.W., *A short history of the steam engine*, second edition, London: Cass, 1963.

Diestalkamp, E.J., 'Richard Turner and the Palm House', Newcomen Society, *Transactions*, volume 54, p. 1–26, 1982.

Emmerson, G.S., *John Scott Russell*, London: Murray, 1977.

Fitzgerald, R., 'The development of the cast iron frame in textile mills to 1850', *Industrial Archaeology Review*, volume 10, 1988, pp. 127–45.

Hamilton, S.B., *A note on the history of reinforced concrete in buildings*, London: HMSO, 1956. (National Building Studies. Special report no. 24.)

Herbert, G., *Pioneers of prefabrication: the British contribution in the nineteenth century*, Baltimore: John Hopkins University Press, 1978.

Hull, R.L., *Power from steam*, Cambridge: University Press, 1989.

Hobhouse, C., *1851 and the Crystal Palace*, London: Murray, 1950.

Institution of Structural Engineers, *Structural engineering: two centuries of British achievement*, Chislehurst: Tarot, for IStructE, 1983.

Joby, R.S., *The railway builders*, Newton Abbot: David and Charles, 1983.

Lewis, M., *Early wooden railways*, Routledge Kegan Paul, 1970.

Mainstone, R., *Development in structural form*, London: Allen Lane, 1975.

Meek, C.L.V., *The railway station*, Yale: University Press, 1957.

Morgan, B., *Civil engineering: railways*, London: Longman, 1971.

Norrie, C.M., *Bridging the years: a short history of British civil engineering*, London: Arnold, 1956.

Pannell, J.P.M., *An illustrated history of civil engineering*, London: Thames and Hudson, 1964.

Pugsley, Sir A., ed., *The works of Isambard Kingdom Brunel*, London, Bristol: ICE, Bristol University, 1976.

Reed, M.C., ed., *Railways in the Victorian economy*, Newton Abbot: David and Charles, 1969.

Rolt, L.T.C., *George and Robert Stephenson*, London: Longman, 1960.

Rolt, L.T.C., *Isambard Kingdom Brunel*, London: Longman, 1958.

Rolt, L.T.C., *Victorian engineering*, London: Allen Lane, 1970.

Scott, J.S., *The Penguin Dictionary of Civil Engineering*, fourth edition, London: Penguin, 1991.

Skempton, A.W., 'Portland cements 1843–87', Newcomen Society, *Transactions*, volume 35, 1962–3, pp. 117–53.

Skempton, A. W., 'Landmarks in early soil mechanics', *Design parameters in soil mechanics, 7th ECSMFE*, volume 5, 1979, pp. 1–26.

Smith, D., 'David Kirkaldy and engineering materials testing', Newcomen Society, *Transactions*, volume 57, 1980–81, pp. 49–66.

Sutherland, R.J.M., 'The introduction of structural wrought iron', Newcomen Society, *Transactions*, volume 36, 1963–4.

Warren, J.G.H., *A century of locomotive building*, 1823– 93, London: A. Reid, 1923.

Watson, J.G., *The Civils: the story of the Institution of Civil Engineers*, London: Thomas Telford Limited, 1988.

CONTEMPORARY SOURCES

Bourne, J., *A treatise on the steam engine*, 1st–11th editions, London: Longman, 1846–76.

Bourne, J.C., *Drawings of the London and Birmingham Railway*, London: Bourne, 1839.

Bourne, J.C., *The history and description of the Great Western Railway*, London: Bogue, 1846.

Brees, S.C., *Railway practice*, 1–4 series, London: J. Williams, 1837–47.

Brunel, I., *The life of Isambard Kingdom Brunel*, London: Longman, 1870.

Clegg, S., *A practical treatise on the manufacture and distribution of coal gas*, 1st–5th editions, London, 1841–68.

Conder, H.R., *Personal recollections of English engineers*, London: Hodder and Stoughton, 1868. Reprinted as *The men who built railways*, London: Thomas Telford Limited.

Copperthwaite, W.C., *Tunnel shields and the use of compressed air in subaqueous works*, London: Constable, 1906.

Cresy, E., *An encyclopaedia of civil engineering*, 2 volumes and supplement, London: Longman, 1847.

Dempsey, G.D., *The practical railway engineer*, fourth edition, London: J Weale, 1856.

Devey, J., *The life of Joseph Locke*, London: Bentley, 1862.

Downes, C. and Cowper, C., *The building erected in Hyde Park for the Great Exhibition*, London: Weale, 1851–2.

Fairbairn, Sir W., *On the application of cast and wrought iron to building purposes*, 1st–4th editions, London: J. Weale, 1854–70.

Haskoll, W.D., *Railway construction*, 2 volumes, London: Atchley, 1857–64.

Helps, A., *The life and labours of Mr Brassey*, London: Bell and Daldy, 1872.

Jackson, T., *Industry illustrated: a memoir of Thomas Jackson*, London: privately published, 1884.

McDermott, F., *The life and work of Joseph Firbank, railway contractor*, London: Longman, 1887.

Moseley, H., *The mechanical principles of engineering and architecture*, London: Longman, 1843.

Newbigging, T., *King's treatise on the science and practice of the manufacture and distribution of coal gas*, 3 volumes, London: King, 1878–83.

Peto, H., *Sir Morton Peto: a memorial sketch*, London: Elliot Stock, 1893.

Potter, H., *Concrete: its uses in building*, London: Spon, 1877.

Rankine, W.J.M., *Manual of applied mechanics*, London: Grafton, 1858.

Rankine, W.J.M., *A manual of civil engineering*, London: Grafton, 1861.

Russell, J.S., *The modern system of naval architecture*, 3 volumes, London: Day, 1865.

Simms, F.W. and Clark, D.K., *Practical tunnelling*,

1st–3rd editions, London: Crosby Lockwood, 1844–91.

Simms, F.W., *A treatise on the principles and practice of levelling*, first edition, London: J. Weale, 1837– .

Stevenson, J., *The principles and practice of river and canal engineering*, second edition, Edinburgh: Black, 1872.

Tredgold, T., *Elementary principles of carpentry*, third edition, London: J. Weale, 1840.

Tredgold, T., *A practical essay on the strength of cast iron*, fourth edition, 2 volumes, London: J. Weale, 1842–6.

Tredgold, T., *The steam engine*, first edition, London: J. Taylor, 1827. Later editions published by J. Weale, 1838, 1840– 44.

Vernon-Harcourt, L.F., *Rivers and canals*, Oxford: Clarendon, 1896.

Walker, T.A., *The Severn tunnel: its construction and difficulties*, London: R. Bentley, 1891.

Walmisley, A.T., *Iron roofs*, London: Spon, 1884.

Whishaw, F., *Railways of Great Britain and Ireland*, London: Simpkin Marshall, 1840.

CHAPTER FOUR

Coad, J.G., *Historic architecture of HM Naval Base, Portsmouth, 1700–1800*, Greenwich: National Maritime Museum, 1981.

Coad, J.G., *Historic architecture of Chatham Dockyard, 1700–1880*, Greenwich: National Maritime Museum, 1982.

Coad, J.G., *The Royal Dockyards 1690–1850: architecture and engineering works of a sailing navy*, Aldershot: Scholar Press, 1989.

Physick, J., *Photography and the South Kensington Museum*, London: Victoria and Albert Museum, 1975.

Skempton, A.W., 'The Boat Store, Sheerness (1858–1860) and its place in structural history', Newcomen Society, *Transactions*, volume 32, 1959–60, pp. 57–75.

Sutherland, R.J.M., 'Shipbuilding and the long span roof', Newcomen Society, *Transactions*, volume 60, pp. 107–26.

Weiler, J., 'The making of collaborative genius: Royal Engineers and structural iron 1820–1870', in 'The Iron Revolution', essays to accompany an exhibition at RIBA, 1990; a summary of part of a DPhil thesis, University of York, 1987.

CONTEMPORARY SOURCES

Serials

Builder, volume 1, 1843–.

Corps of the Royal Engineers: Professional Papers, 1837–95.

Institution of Civil Engineers, Minutes of Proceedings, volume 1, 1837–1935.

Royal Engineers Journal, volume 1, 1870.

Royal Institute of British Architects, *Transactions*, volume 1, 1834–.

Books

Barlow, P., *An essay on the strength and stress of timber*, 1st–3rd editions, London: J. Taylor, 1817–28.

Barlow, P., *A treatise of the strength of timber, cast iron, malleable iron and other materials*, 4th–7th editions, London: J. Weale, 1837–67.

Chatham Lectures, *Lectures presented at the Royal Engineers Establishment*, *c.* 1867–74.

Connolly, T. W. J., *History of the Royal Sappers and miners*, 1772 and 1856, 2 volumes, London: Longman, 1857.

Douglas, H., *An essay on the principles and construction of military bridges*, 1st–3rd editions, London: J. Murray, 1816–53.

Pasley, C.W., *A course of elementary fortification*, second edition, 2 volumes, London: Murray, 1822.

Pasley, C.W., *Observations on limes, calcareous cements, mortars, stuccos and concrete*, London: J. Weale, 1838, second edition 1847.

Pasley, C.W., *Outline of a course of practical architecture*, Chatham, 1862, reprint of 1826 edition.

Porter, W., *History of the Corps of Royal Engineers*, 2 volumes, London: Longman, 1889.

Scott, General, 'On the construction of the Albert Hall', RIBA, *Transactions*, 22 January 1872, pp. 82–100.

Unwin, W.C., *Wrought iron bridges and roofs*, London: Spon, 1869.

Vicat, L.J., (trans. Smith, J.T.), *A Practical and scientific treatise on calcareous mortars and cements*, London: J. Weale, 1837.

Young, C.D. and Company, *Illustrations of iron structures for home and abroad*, Edinburgh: C.D. Young and Company, *c.* 1850.

CHAPTER FIVE

Berridge, P.S.A., *The girder bridge after Brunel and others*, London: R. Maxwell, 1969.

Booth, L.G., 'Laminated timber arch railway bridges in England and Scotland', Newcomen Society, *Transactions*, volume 44, pp. 1–23.

De Mare, E., *The bridges of Britain*, London: Batsford, 1954.

Douglas, H., *Crossing the Forth*, London: R. Hale, 1964.

Hammond, R., *The Forth Bridge and its builders*, London: Eyre and Spottiswoode, 1964.

Hopkins, H.S., *A span of bridges*, Newton Abbot: David and Charles, 1970.

James, J.G., 'Some steps in the evolution of early iron arched bridge designs', Newcomen Society, *Transactions*, volume 59, 1987–8, pp. 153–87.

James, J.G., 'The evolution of iron bridge trusses to 1850', Newcomen Society, *Transactions*, volume 52, 1980–1, pp. 67–101.

James, J.G., 'The evolution of wooden bridge trusses to 1850', Institution of Wood Science, *Journal*, 1982, pp. 116–35, 168–93.

James, J.G., 'The origins and worldwide spread of Warren-truss bridges in the mid-nineteenth century, Part 1', *History of technology*, volume 11, 1987, pp. 65–123.
MacKay, S., *The Forth Bridge: a picture history*, Edinburgh: Mowbray House, 1990.
Murray, A., *The Forth Railway Bridge: a celebration*, Edinburgh: Mainstream, 1983.
Paxton, R., ed., *100 years of the Forth Bridge*, London: Thomas Telford, 1990.
Prebble, J., *The high girders*, Secker and Warburg, 1956.
Pugsley, Sir A., ed., *The works of Isambard Kingdom Brunel*, London: ICE, Bristol: University Press, 1976. Reprinted by Cambridge University Press.
Richards, Sir J.H., *The National Trust book of bridges*, London: J. Cape, 1984.
Rosenberg, N. and Vincenti, W.G., *The Britannia Bridge: the generation and diffusion of technological knowledge*, Cambridge, Mass.: MIT, 1978.
Shipway, J.S., *The Tay Railway Bridge 1887–1987*, Edinburgh: ICE East of Scotland Local Association, 1987.
Thomas, J., *The Tay Bridge disaster*, Newton Abbot: David and Charles, 1972.

CONTEMPORARY SOURCES

Serials

The Builder, 1843–(*as Building*).
Civil engineer and architects journal, 1837–68.
The Engineer, 1856–.
Engineering, 1866–.
Industries, 1886–93.
Institution of Civil Engineers, Minutes of Proceedings, 1837–1935.
Institution of Civil Engineers, Transactions, 1836–42.
Society of Engineers, Transactions, 1860–.

Books

Arrol, Sir W. and Company, *Bridges*, London: Engineering, 1909.
Baker, B., *Long span bridges*, London: Engineering, 1867.
Baker, B., 'The Forth Bridge', *Iron and Steel Institute Journal*, No. 11, 1885.
Baker, B., 'The Forth Bridge', British Association Lecture, 1885.
Baker, B., 'Bridging the Firth of Forth', Royal Institution Lecture, 1887.
Barlow, C., *The New Tay Bridge*, London: Spon, 1889.
Birkhausen, G., *Die Forthbrücke*, Berlin: Springer, 1889.
Bow, R.H., *A treatise on bracing*, published privately, 1851.
Bow, R.H., *Economics of construction in relation to framed structures*, London: Spon, 1873.
Brunel, I.K., *The life of Isambard Kingdom Brunel, civil engineer*, London: Longman, 1870.
Clark, E., *Britannia and Conway tubular bridges*, London: Longman, 1850.
Commission appointed to inquire into the application of iron into railway structures Report, London: HMSO, 1849.
Fairbairn, W., *An account of the Britannia and Conwy tubular bridges*, London: Weale/Longman, 1849.
Grothe, A., *The Tay Bridge*, Dundee: J. Leng, 1878.
Haskoll, W.D., *Examples of bridge and viaduct construction*, first and second editions, London: Lockwood, 1864, 1867.
Humber, W., *A complete treatise on cast and wrought iron bridge construction*, three editions, 2 volumes, London, 1861–70.
Humber, W., *A practical treatise on cast and wrought iron bridges*, London: Spon, 1857.
Jeaffreason, J.S., *The life of Robert Stephenson*, 2 volumes, London: Longman, 1864.
Latham, J.H., *Construction of wrought iron bridges, etc.*, Cambridge: University Press, 1858.
MacKay, J., *The life of Sir John Fowler, engineer*, London: Murray, 1900.
Matheson, E., *Works in iron, bridges and roof structures*, London: Spon, 1873.
Maw, W.H. and Dredge, J., *Modern examples of road and rail bridges*, London: Engineering, 1873.
Maynard, H.N., *Handbook to the Crumlin Viaduct*, Crumlin: J.M. Wilson, 1862.
Phillips, P., *The Forth Bridge in all its stages of construction*, Edinburgh: Grant, R., 1890.
Tarbotton, M.O., *History of the old Trent Bridge with a descriptive account of the New Bridge, Nottingham*, Nottingham: 1871.
Weale, J., ed., *The theory, practice and architecture of bridges*, 4 volumes and supplement, London: J. Weale, 1839–43, 1852–3.
Westhofen, W., *The Forth Bridge*, London: Engineering, 1890.

CHAPTER SIX

Barker, T.C. and Robbins, M., *A history of London Transport, vol.1*, London: Allen and Unwin, 1962.
Betjeman, J., *London's historic railway stations*, London: J. Murray, 1972.
Course, E., *London railways*, London: Batsford, 1962.
Hunter, M. and Thorne, R., eds., *Change at King's Cross: from 1800 to the present*, London: Historical Publications, 1990.
Jackson, A.A., *London's termini*, Newton Abbot: David and Charles, 1985.
Jackson, A.A., *London's local railways*, Newton Abbot: David and Charles, 1978.
Jackson, A.A. and Croome, D., *Rails through the clay*, London: Allen and Unwin, 1962.
Kellett, J.R., *The impact of railways on Victorian cities*, London: 1969.
Simmons, J., *St Pancras Station*, London: Allen and Unwin, 1968.
Tucker, M., 'Bricklayers Arms Station', *London's Industrial Archaeology*, volume 4, 1989, pp. 1–23.
White, H. P., *A regional history of the railways of Great Britain, vol. 3, Greater London*, London: Phoenix House/David and Charles, 1963.

CONTEMPORARY SOURCES

Serials

Builder, volume 1, 1843–.

Civil engineer and architects journal, volumes 1–31, 1837–68.

Engineer, volume 1, 1856–.

Engineering, volume 1–, 1866–.

Illustrated London News, 1842–.

Institution of Civil Engineers, Minutes of Proceedings, volume 1–, 1837–1935.

Railway journal/magazine (Herapeth's), volume 1–, 1832–1893.

Railway news, volume 1, 1864–1918.

Railway times, volume 1, 1838–1914.

Society of Engineers, Transactions, 1860–.

CHAPTER SEVEN

Baldwin, M.W., 'Engineering history of Hull's earliest docks', Newcomen Society, *Transactions*, volume 46, 1973–4, pp. 1–12.

Clark, E.F., *George Parker Bidder*, Bedford: KSL, 1983.

Guillery, F., 'Building the Millwall Docks', *Construction history*, volume 6, 1990, pp. 3–22.

Neale, W.G., *At the port of Bristol*, 2 volumes, Bristol: Port Authority, 1968–70.

North East London Polytechnic, *Dockland: an illustrated history of life and work in East London*, London: NELP/GLC, 1986.

Pudney, J., *London's docks*, London: Thames and Hudson, 1975.

Rennison, R. W., 'The development of the North East coal ports', 1987. PhD thesis partly summarized in his presidential address to the Newcomen Society, 1991.

Ritchie-Noakes, N., *Jesse Hartley: dock engineer to the port of London, 1824–1860*, Liverpool: Merseyside County Council, 1980.

Ritchie-Noakes, N., *Liverpool's historic waterfront*, London: HMSO, 1984.

Sargent, E., 'Frederick Eliot Duckham, MICE, and the Millwall Docks (1868–1909)', Newcomen Society, *Transactions*, volume 60, 1988–9, pp. 49–71.

Skempton, A.W., 'Engineering in the port of London 1807', Newcomen Society, *Transactions*, volume 50, 1978–9, pp. 87–108.

Skempton, A.W., 'Engineering in the port of London 1808–1834', Newcomen Society, *Transactions*, volume 53, 1981–2, pp. 73–96.

CONTEMPORARY SOURCES

Serials

Artizan, volumes 1–28, 1844–71.

Civil engineer and architects journal, volumes 1–31, 1837–68.

Engineer, volume 1, 1856–.

Engineering, volume 1, 1866–.

Institution of Civil Engineers, Transactions, volumes 1–3, 1836–42.

Institution of Civil Engineers, *Minutes of Proceedings*, volume 1, 1837–1935.

Institution of Engineers and Shipbuilders in Scotland Transactions, volume 1, 1888–.

Liverpool Engineering Society, volume 1, 1881.

North East Coast Institution of Engineers, volume 1, 1885.

Books

Abernethy, J.S., *The life and work of James Abernethy*, London: Brettell, 1897.

Allen, J.R., *Theory and practice in the design and construction of dock walls*, London: Spon, 1876.

Leech, Sir B., *History of the Manchester Ship Canal*, 2 volumes, Manchester: Sherratt and Hughes, 1907.

Rennie, Sir J., *Autobiography*, London: Spon, 1875.

Rennie, Sir J., *The theory, formation and construction of British and foreign harbours*, 2 volumes, London: J. Weale, 1854.

Stevenson, A., *Account of the Skerryvore Lighthouse*, Edinburgh: Black, 1848.

Stevenson, A., *A rudimentary treatise on lighthouses*, London: J. Weale, 1850.

Stevenson, D., *Life of Robert Stevenson*, Edinburgh: Black, 1878.

Stevenson, R.L., *Records of a family of engineers*, London: Chatto and Windus, 1924.

Stevenson, T., *The design and construction of harbours*, third edition, Edinburgh: Black, 1886.

Stevenson, T., *Lighthouse construction and illumination*, London: Spon, 1881.

Vernon-Harcourt, L.F., *Harbours and docks*, 2 volumes, Oxford: Clarendon, 1885.

CHAPTER EIGHT

Binnie, G.M., *Early Victorian water engineers*, London: TTL, 1981.

Binnie, G.M., *Early dam builders in Britain*, London: TTL, 1987.

Binnie, G.M., 'Masonry and concrete dams 1880–1941', *Industrial archaeology review*, volume X, 1987, pp. 41–58.

Davidson, I., 'George Deacon (1843–1909) and the Vyrnwy works', Newcomen Society, *Transactions*, volume 59, 1987–8, pp. 81–95.

Hartley, D., *Water in England*, London: Macdonald, 1964.

Hoyle, N., *Reservoirs from Rivington to Rossendale*, Bolton: North Western Water, 1987.

Rennison, R.W., *Water to Tyneside*, Newcastle: Newcastle and Gateshead Water Company, 1977.

Russell, P., 'John Frederick de la Trobe Bateman (1810–1889) water engineer', Newcomen Society, *Transactions*, volume 52, 1980–1, pp. 119–38.

Skempton, A. W, 'Historical development of British embankment dams to 1960',*Clay Barriers for Embankment Dams*, ICE Conference, London: TTL, 1990, pp. 15–52.

Smith, D., 'Sir Joseph William Bazalgette', Newcomen Society, *Transactions*, volume 58, 1986–7, pp. 89–111.

Smith, N.A.F., *History of dams*, London: Peter Davies, 1971.

Stanbridge, H.N., *History of sewage treatment*, 11 volumes, Maidstone: IWPC, 1976.

CONTEMPORARY SOURCES

Serials

[Incorporated] Association of Municipal Engineers, *Proceedings*, 1875–1983 (continued as the *Municipal Engineer*).
Builder, volume 1, 1843–.
Engineer, volume 1, 1856–.
Engineering, volume 1, 1866–.
Gas and water review, volume 1–23, 1879–89.
Institution of Civil Engineers, *Minutes of Proceedings*, volume 1, 1837–1935.
Journal of gas lighting and water supply, volume 1–, 1849–1914.
(Royal) Sanitary Institute (now Royal Society of Health, *Journal (Transactions)*, 1877–.

Books

Bateman, J.F. La T., *The history and description of the Manchester waterworks*, London: Spon, 1884.
Beloe, C.H., *On the construction of catchwater reservoirs in mountain districts*, London: Spon, 1872.
Boulnois, H.P., *The municipal and sanitary engineers handbook*, London: Spon, 1883.
Burton, W.K., *The water supply of towns*, London: Crosby Lockwood, 1894.
Denton, J.B., *Sanitary engineering*, London: Spon, 1877.
Gale, J.M., *Glasgow waterworks*, Glasgow: Institution of Engineers and Shipbuilders, 1864.
Hughes, S., *A treatise on waterworks for the supply of cities and towns*, 1st–3rd editions, London: J. Weale, (Lockwood) 1856–75.
Latham, B., *Sanitary engineering*, London: Spon, 1873.
Tudsberry Turner, J.H. and Brightmore, A.W., *The principles of waterworks engineering*, London: Spon, 1893.

CHAPTER NINE

Brotherson, W.H., *Historical aspects of the port of Botany Bay*, Sydney: AIM, 1962.
Carroll, B., *The engineers: 200 years at work for Australia*, Barton, ACT: Institution of Engineers 1988.
Cumming, D.A., *Australia's engineering heritage*, Adelaide: University, 1979.
Harrigan, L.J., *Victorian railways to 1962*, Melbourne: Victorian Railways Public Relations Board, 1962.
Lay, M.G., paper in *Australian Road Research Board, 14th Congress*, 1988.
National Association of Australian State Road Authorities, *Bush track to highway: 200 years of Australian roads*, Sydney: NAASRA, 1987.
Nock, O.S., *Railways of Australia*, London: A. and C. Black, 1971.
O'Connor, C., *Spanning two centuries: historic bridges of Australia,* St Lucia, Queensland: University of Queensland Press, 1985.
Phillips, V., *Bridges and ferries of Australia,* Sydney: Bay Books, 1983.
Singleton, C.C. and Burke, D., *Railways of Australia*, Sydney: Angus and Robertson, 1967.
Stephenson, P.R., *History and description of Sydney Harbour*, Adelaide: Rigby Limited, 1967.
Taunton, M., *The chief: C.Y. O'Connor,* Nedlands: University of Western Australia, 1978.
Underwood, R.T., *A history of traffic in Australia*, Nunawading, Victoria: ARRB, 1989.

CONTEMPORARY SOURCES

The main contemporary published sources are the reports of the government engineers and public works departments of the various states.

Serials

Australian Association for the Advancement of Science, volume 1, 1885–.
Australian Surveyor, 1888–.
Engineer, volume 1, 1856–.
Engineering, volume 1, 1866–
Institution of Civil Engineers, *Minutes of Proceedings*, volume 1, 1837–1935.
Royal Society of New South Wales, *Proceedings*, volume 1, 1858–.
Victoria Assocation of Engineers, *Proceedings*, volume 1–, 1883–1938.

CHAPTER TEN

Allen, C. J., *Switzerland's amazing railways*, London: T. Nelson, 1953.
Amouroux, D., 'L'age d'or des ponts suspendus en France 1823–1850', *Annales des ponts et chaussées*, 1981, third edition, pp. 53–63.
Armand, L., *Historie des chemins de fer en France*, Paris: Presses Modernes, 1963.
Artola, M., ed., *Los Ferrocarilles en España, 1844–1943*, 2 volumes, Madrid: Banco des España, 1978.
Blaser, W., *Schweizer Holzbrücken/wooden bridges in Switzerland*, Basel: Birkhauser, 1982.
Briand, I., *Stori delle ferrorie in Italia*, 3 volumes, Milan: Cavallotti, 1977.
Brulhart, A., *Guillaime Henri Dufour: genie civil et urbanisme à Geneve an XIXe Siècle*, Lausanne: Payot, 1989.
Brunot, A., and Coruand, R., *Le Corps des Ponts et Chaussées*, Paris: CNRS, 1982.
Comision Oficial para la Commemoracion del Primer centenrio del Ferrocarril en España, *Cien Años de ferrocarril España*, 4 volumes, Madrid: Comision, 1948.
Dartsch, B., *Jahrhundertbaustoff Stahlbeton*, Düsseldorf: Beton Verlag, 1984.
Deutsche Reichsbahn, *Hundert Jahre deutsche Eisenbahnen*, Berlin: Deutsche Reichsbahn, 1936.
Deutscher Verband für Wasserwirtschaft und Kulturbau, *Historische Talsperren*, Stuttgart: Konrad Wittwer, 1987.

Ferjencik, P. and Hruban, I.B., 'Bedrich Schnirch', *Dejiny ved a technicky*, volume 16, 1983, pp. 4–17.
Fernandez Ordonez, J. A., *Catalogo de noventa Presas y Azundes Espanoles anteriores de 1900*, Madrid: CEHOPU, 1984.
Fischer, J. and O., *Prazske mosty*, Prague: Academia, 1985.
Gall, I., *Regi magyar hidak*, Budapest: Muszaki Kony & Kiado, 1970.
Garbrecht, G., ed., *Hydraulics and hydraulic research: a historical review*, Rotterdam: Balkema, 1987.
Halasz, R. von, *Beiträge zur Bautechnik*, Berlin: Ernst, 1980.
Harriss, J., *The Eiffel Tower*, London: Elek, 1976.
Hartley, C. W. S., *A biography of Sir Charles Hartley, civil engineer (1825–1915): the father of the Danube*, Lampeter: Edwin Mellen, 1989.
Hartung, G., *Eisenkonstuktionen des 19. Jahrhunderts*, Munich: Schinner-Mosel, 1983.
Hruban, I. B., 'Retezovy most ve Straznici', *Stavebnicky Casopis*, volume 12, 1974, pp. 673–87.
James, J. G., 'Russian iron bridges to 1850', Newcomen Society, *Transactions*, volume 54, 1982–3, pp. 79–104.
Jankowski, J., *Mosty w Polsce i mostonvcy Polscy*, Wroclaw: Polska Akademia Nauk, 1973.
Jarnvagsstyrelse, *Statens Jarnvagar 1856–1906*, 4 volumes, Stockholm, 1906.
Josef, D., *Mosty: nase mosty historicke a soucasne*, Prague: NADAS, 1984.
Jurecka, C., *Brücken*, Vienna: Anton Schroll, 1986.
Klee, W., *Preussische Eisenbahngeschichte*, Stuttgart: Kohlhamner, 1982.
Kurrer, K.E., 'Die Baustatik in Frankreich und Deutschland im frühen 19 Jahrhundert', *Humanismus und Technik*, Jahrbuch 1986/7.
Kurrer, K.E., 'Der Beitrag Emil Winklers zur Herausbildung der Klassischen', *Humanismus und Technik*, Jahrbuch, 1987/8.
Kurrer, K.E., 'Zur Frühgeschichte des Stahlbetonbaues in Deutschland: 100 Jahre Monier Brochure', *Beton und Stahlbetonbau*, volume 83, 1, 1988.
Kurrer, K.E., 'Zur Geschichte der Theorie der Nebenspannungen in Fachwerken: Otto Mohr zum 150 Geburtstag', *Bautechnik*, 1985.
Lemoine, B., *Gustave Eiffel*, Paris: Hazen, 1984.
Loyrette, H., *Gustave Eiffel*, New York: Rizzoli, 1985.
Mayer, A. von, *Geschichte und Geographie der Deutschen Eisenbahnen, von 1835–1890*, 2 volumes, Moers: Steiger, reprint 1984.
Mehrtens, G., *Die Deutsche Brückenbau in XIX Jahrhundert*, Dusseldorf: VDI, reprint 1984.
Mislin, M., *Geschichte der Baukonstruktion und Bautechnik*, Düsseldorf: Werner, 1988.
Mislin, M., 'Zur Konstruktionsgeschichte der ersten Hängedächer in 19 Jahrhundert', *Technikgesichte*, volume 52, 1985, pp. 25–48.
O'Brien, P., ed., *Railways and the economic development of Western Europe, 1830–1914*, New York: St Martin's Press, 1983.
Peters, T.F., *Transitions in engineering: Guillaime Henri Dufour and the early 19th century cable suspension bridges*, Basel: Birkhauser, 1987.
Pottgiesser, H., *Eisenbahnbrücken aus zwei Jahrhunderten*, Basel: Birkhauser, 1985.
Prade, M., *Ponts et viaducts au XIXe Siècle*, Poitou: Brissaud, 1988.
Sandstrom, K.E., *The history of tunnelling*, London: Barrie and Rockcliff, 1963.
Thiessing, R. and Paschoud, M., eds., *Les chemins de fer suisses après un siècle, 1847–1947*, 5 volumes, Neufchatel: Delachaux and Niestle, 1949.
Vandenberghen, J., *La Naissance et d'evolution des chemins de fer de l'état Belge et des reseaux concedés*, Brussels: SNCB, 1985.
Werner, E., *Die ersten Ketten- und Drahtseilbrucken*, Düsseldorf: VDI, 1973.
Werner, E., *Technisierung des Bauens*, Düsseldorf: Werner, 1980.
Westwood, J. N., *A history of Russian railways*, London: Allen and Unwin, 1964.
Wissenschaften in Berlin, 3 volumes, Berlin: Technische Universität, 1987.

CONTEMPORARY SOURCES

Serials

Austria–Hungary
Allgemeine Bauzeitung, volume 1, 1836–.
A magyar mernok, volume 1, 1867–1941.
Österreichicher Ingenieur- und Architekten-Verein, Zeitung, etc., volume 1, 1849–.

Belgium
Annales des travaux publics de Belgique, volume 1, 1843–.

Czechoslovakia
Architeken und Ingenieurien Verein in Böhmen, Mitteilungen (Zpravy spolku), volume 1–, 1866–1901.
Technische Blätter, volume 1–, 1869–1921.

Denmark
Teknisk Forening, Tidsskrift, volume 1, 1877–1941.

France
Annales des constructeurs des ponts et chaussées, volumes 1–35, 1858–91.
Annales des ponts et chaussées, volume 1, 1831–.
Annales du genie civil, volumes 1–20, 2e seri, volumes 1– 9, 1862–80.
Annales des travaux publics, volume 1, 1880–1906.
Annuaire des ponts et chaussées, 1804, 1806–1831.
Genie civil, vol. 1, 1880–1973.
Journal des chemins de fer, volume 1, 1842–.
Journal du genie civil, volumes 1–16, 1828–48.
Nouvelles annales de construction, volume 1, 1855–1903.
Révue Generale des chemins de fer, volume 1, 1878–.
Sociefe des ingenieurs civils de France, *Memoires*, 1848–1965.

Germany
Architekten und Ingenieurs Verein in Hanover, Notizblatt, volumes 1–3, Zeitschrift, volume 1–, 1851–95.

Centralblatt der Bauverwaltung, volume 1, 1881–1944.
Der (Civil) ingenieur, volume 1, 1848–96.
Deutsche Bauzeitung, volume 1, 1867–.
Eisenbahn Zeitung, volumes 1–19, 1843–61.
Journal für die Baukunst, 1829–38.
Journal für Gas beleuchtung, volume 1, 1858–1920.
Verein Deutscher Ingenieurs, Zeitschrift, volume 1, 1857–.
Zeitschrift für Baukunde, volumes 1–7, 1878–84.
Zeitschrift für Bauwesen, volume 1, 1851–1931.
Zeitschrift für praktische Baukunst, volume 1–41, 1841–81.

Italy

Giornale del genio civil, 1863–.
Giornale dell ingegnere, volumes 1–16, 1853–68.
Il Politecnico, volume 1, 1839–1937.

Netherlands

Koninlijk Instituut van Ingenieurs, *Verhandelingen, 1848–93*.
De Ingenieur, volume 1, 1886–.

Norway

Polyteknisk tidsskrift (now *Teknisk ukblad*), volume 1, 1854–.

Portugal

Revista de obras publicas e minas, volume 1–, 1870–1926.

Russia

Journal des voies et communication, volumes 1–36, 1826–36.
Zhurnal putei soobshcheniya (glavnoego upravleniya . . .) volume 1–, 1826–1917.

Spain

Anales de obras publics, volume 1, 1876–84.
Revista de obras publicas, volume 1, 1853–.

Sweden

Teknisk tidskrift (now *Ny teknik*), volume 1, 1871–.
Ingeniors-Forening, Forhandlingar, volume 1–, 1865–1890.
Tidskrift for svenska ingenieurer, volumes 1–2, 1851–2.
Tidskrift fur teknologi, volumes 1–9, 1859–67.

Switzerland

Chemin de fer/Eisenbahn, volume 1–, 1874–82.
Schweizerische Bauzeitung, 1883–.

Books

Dupin, C., *Voyages dans la Grande Bretagne . . . en 1816, 1817 et 1819*, 3 volumes and atlas, Paris, 1820.
Dutens, J., *Memoires sur les travaux publics de l'Angleterre*, Paris, 1819.
Eiffel, G., *Notice sur le pont du Douro*, Clichy: Chemin de fer de Paul Dupont, 1819.
Eiffel, G., *La Tour de trois centre metres*, 2 volumes, Paris: Société des Impermerie Lemecier, 1900.
Heinzerling, F., *Die Brücken in Eisen*, Berlin: Springer, 1870.
Morandière, R., *Traité de la construction des ponts*, first and second editions, 3 volumes, Paris, 1874, 1880–8.
Navier, C.L.M.H., *Memoire sur les ponts suspendus*, Paris: Imprimerie Royale, 1823.
Navier, C.L.M.H., *Resumé des leçons données a l'École des Ponts et Chaussées*, 1st–3rd editions, Paris: Didot, etc., 1826–64.
Schnirch, F. and J., *Beytrag fur den Kettenbrückenbau*, Prague: Gerzabek, 1832.
Wayss, G. A., *Das System Monier*, Berlin: Seydel, 1887.
Winkler, E., *Vorträge über Brückenbau*, 5 volumes, Vienna: Gerold, 1875–81.
Winkler, E., *Vorträge über Eisenbahnbau*, 5 volumes, Prague: Dominians, 1874–8.

CHAPTER ELEVEN

Berridge, P.S.A., *Couplings to the Khyber*, Newton Abbot: David and Charles, 1969.
Brown, J., 'Contributions of the British to irrigation engineering in upper India in the nineteenth century', Newcomen Society, *Transactions*, volume 55, 1983–4, pp. 85–112.
Brown, J., 'Sir Proby Cautley (1802–71), a Pioneer of Indian Irrigation', *History of Technology*, volume 3, 1978.
James, J.G., 'The Origins and spread of Warren-truss bridges in the mid-nineteenth century (part 1: Origins)', *History of Technology*, volume 11, 1986, pp. 65–124.
James, J.G., *Overseas Railways and the Spread of Iron Bridges c. 1850–1870*, Strawberry Hill: J.G. James, 1987.
Ministry of Railways, *History of Indian Railways . . . up to 31 March 1955*, Simla: GPO, 1958.
Public Works Department, *Triennial Review of Irrigation in India 1918–1921*, Simla: GPO, 1921.
Sandes, E.W.S., *The Military Engineer in India*, 2 volumes, Chatham: Institution of Royal Engineers.

CONTEMPORARY SOURCES

Serials

Institution of Civil Engineers, *Minutes of Proceedings*, 1837–1935.
Professional Papers on Indian Engineering, 1866–86.
Engineers Journal (Calcutta), 1858–69 Continued as:
Indian Engineer, 1886–.
Engineer, 1856–.
Engineering, 1866–.
Professional Papers of the Madras Engineers, 1839–1856.

Books

Booth, R.B., *Life and work in India*, London: Hammond, 1912.
Brereton, R.M., *Reminiscences of an Old English Civil Engineer 1858–1908*, Portland, Oregon: Irwin Hudson, 1908.
Brunton, J., *John Brunton's Book*, Cambridge: University Press, 1939.
Burge, C.O., *The adventures of a civil engineer*, London: Alston Rivers, 1909.
Davidson, E., *The Railways of India*, London: Spon, 1868.
Hope, Lady E.R., *General Sir Arthur Cotton*, London: Hodder and Stoughton, 1900.

James, C.C., *Drainage Problems in the East*, Bombay: Bennett, Coleman and Company, 1917.
Molesworth, E.J., *Life of Sir Guildford L. Molesworth*, London: Spon, 1922.
Robertson, George, *Reports to the Government of India on Indian harbours*, 2 parts, Edinburgh: 1871–3.
Willcocks, Sir W., *Sixty years in the East*, Edinburgh: Blackwood, 1935.

CHAPTER TWELVE

Albion, R.G., *The rise of New York Port, 1815–1860*, Newton Abbot: David and Charles, 1970 reprint.
Allen, R.S., *Covered bridges of the Midwest (Middle Atlanta States, North East South)*, Lexington, Mass.: S. Greene, 1957.
American Public Works Association. *History of public works in the United States*, Chicago: APWA, 1976.
American Society of Civil Engineers, *A biographical dictionary of American civil engineers*, 2 volumes, New York: ASCE, 1972–91.
Berton, P., *The impossible railways: the building of the Canadian Pacific*, New York: Knopf, 1972.
Calhoun, D.H., *The American civil engineer: origins and conflict*, Cambridge, Mass.: Harvard University Press, 1960.
Condit, C.W., *American building art in the nineteenth century*, New York, 1960.
Condit, C.W., *The Chicago School of Architecture*, Chicago: University Press, 1964.
Condit, C.W., *The port of New York: a history of the rail and terminal system from the beginnings to Pennsylvania Station*, Chicago: University Press, 1980.
Currie, A.W., *The Grand Trunk Railway of Canals*, Toronto: University Press, 1957.
Darnell, V.C., *A directory of American bridge building companies 1840–1900*, Washington, DC: SIA, 1984.
Darnell, V.C., *Nathaniel Rider and his iron bridges*, Washington, DC: SIA, 1991.
Drescher, N.M., *Engineers for the public good: US Army Corps of Engineers Buffalo district*, Washington DC: USGPO, 1988.
Edwards, L.N., *A record of history and evolution of early American bridges*, Toronto: University Press, 1989.
Hungerford, E., *The story of the Baltimore and Ohio Railroad, 1827–1927*, New York: Putnams, 1928.
Kemp, E.L., *James Finlay and the modern suspension bridge*, ASCE Preprint 3590, 1979.
Kollgard, E.M. and Chadwick, W.L., *Development of dam engineering in the United States*, New York: Pergamon, 1988.
Kouvvenhoven, J.A., 'The designing of the Eads Bridge', *Technology and Culture*, volume 23, 1982, pp. 535–68.
Lamb, W.K., *History of the Canadian Pacific Railway*, New York: Macmillan, 1977.
Leggett, R.F., *Canals of Canada*, Vancouver: Douglas, 1976.
Leggett, R.F., *The first hundred and fifty years of civil engineering in Canada*, Toronto: Department of Civil Engineering, 1977.
Leggett, R.F., *Ottawa river canals and the defence of British North America*, Toronto: University Press, 1988.
Leggett, R.F., *Railways of Canada*, Newton Abbot: David and Charles, 1973.
Leggett, R.F., *Rideau waterway*, Toronto: University Press, 1967.
Leggett, R.F., 'Thomas Roy and his Remarks on road making (1841)' *Canadian geotechnical journal*, volume 25, 1988, pp. 1–12.
Lewis, G.D., *Charles Ellet, Jr: the engineer industrialist 1818–1862*, Urbana: University of Illinois Press, 1968.
McCullough, D., *The great Bridge*, New York: Simon and Schuster, 1972.
Mills, G.B., *Of men and rivers: the story of the Vicksburg District*, Vicksburg: US Army, 1978.
Morgan, E., *Dams and other disasters: a century of the Army Corps of Engineers in civil works*, Boston: Porter Sargent, 1971.
National Museum of Science and Technology (Canada), *Mind, heart and vision: professional engineering in Canada 1887–1987*, Ontario: National Museum, 1987.
Peterson, C.E., ed., *Building early America*, Radnor, Pa.: Chilton Book Company, 1976.
Randall, F.A., *History of the development of building construction in Chicago*, Urbana: Illinois University Press, 1949.
Sanderton, W.S., *The great national project: a history of the Chesapeake and Ohio canal*, Baltimore: John Hopkins University Press, 1946.
Schodek, D.L., *Landmarks in American civil engineering*, Cambridge: MIT, 1987.
Steinman, D.B., *The builders of the bridge – the story of John Roebling and his son*, New York: Harcourt Brace, 1950.
Trachenborg, A., *Brooklyn Bridge: fact and symbol*, Chicago: University Press, 1929, 1968.
Turhollow, A.F., *History of navigation and navigation improvements on the Pacific Coast*, Washington, DC: USGPO, 1983.
Vogel, R.M., *The engineering contributions of Wendel Bollman*, (contributions paper 36), Washington, DC: Smithsonian Institution, 1964.
Vogel, R.M., *Roebling's Delaware and Hudson canal aqueducts*, Washington, DC: Smithsonian Institution, 1971.

CONTEMPORARY SOURCES

The main published sources for Canada are the Reports of the Public Works Department.

Serials

American railroad journal, 1832–1886.
American Society of Civil Engineers, *Proceedings*, volume 1, 1876–, *Transactions*, volume 1, 1872–.
Canadian Society of Civil Engineers, *Transactions*, volume 1–, 1887–1907.
Engineering and mining journal, volume 1–, 1866–1922.

Engineering news, volume 1–, 1874–.
Engineering Record, volume 1–, 1887– (now combined with *Engineering news* as *Engineering News Record*).
Franklin Institute, *Journal*, first and second series, 1826–.
Railroad gazette, volume 1–, 1873–1908.
Scientific American, volume 1–, 1859–.
Van Nostrand's electric engineering magazine, 1869–1886.

Books

Birkmire, W.H., *Skeleton construction in buildings*, New York: Wiley, 1893.
Culmann, K., 'Der Bau der holzernen Brücken in den Vereinigten Staaten von Amerika', *Allgemeine Bauzeitung*, volume 16, 1851, pp. 169–229.
Culmann, K., 'Der Bau der eisernen Brücken in England und Amerika', *Allgemeine Bauzeitung*, volume 17, 1852, pp. 163–222.
Francis, J.B., *The Lowell hydraulic experiments*, 1st-4th eds., Bolton: Little, Brown and Co., 1855–83.
Freitag, J.K., *Architectural engineering*, New York, 1895.
Gerstner, F.A.R., *Die Innern Communication der Vereignigten Staaten von Nord Amerika*, Prague: 1842–3.
Ghega, C., *Über Nordamerikanische Brückenbau*, Wien: C. Gerolds, 1845.
Gillmore, Q.A., *Practical treatise on limes, hydraulic cements and mortars*, New York: Van Nostrand Reinhold, 1863.
Haupt, H., *General theory of bridge building*, New York: Appleton, 1851.
Hodges, J., *Construction of the great Victoria Bridge in Canada*, London: J. Weale, 1860.
Holley, H.L., *American and European railway practice*, London: The Engineer, 1857.
Humphreys, A.A. and Abbot, H.L., *Report upon physics and hydraulics of the Mississippi*, Philadelphia: Lippincott, 1861.
Hyatt, T.P., *An account of some experiments with Portland cement and iron*, Privately published, 1873.
Mahan, D.H., *An Elementary course of civil engineering*, Glasgow: Fullarton, 1831.
Malezieux, E., *Travaux publics des États-Unis d'Amerique en 1870*, Paris: Dunod, 1873.
Roebling, J.A., *Long and short span railway bridges*, New York: Van Nostrand Reinhold, 1869.
Smalley, E.V., *History of the Northern Pacific Railroad*, New York: Putnams, 1883.
Strickland, W.B., *Reports on canals, railways, roads and other subjects . . . ,* Philadelphia: Carey and Lea, 1826.
Stuart, C.B., *Lives and works of civil engineers of America*, New York: Van Nostrand Reinhold, 1871.
Weale, J., ed. comp., *Papers and practical illustrations of public works of recent construction both British and American*, London: J. Weale, 1856.
Wegmann, E., *The design and construction of masonry dams*, New York: J. Wiley, 1888.
Whipple, S., *A Work on bridge building*, Utica: H.H. Curtiss, 1847.
Woodward, C.N., *A history of the St Louis Bridge*, St Louis: G.I. Jones, 1881.

CHAPTER THIRTEEN

American Society of Civil Engineers, *Biographical dictionary of American civil engineers*, NY: ASCE, 1972.
Centro Argentino de Ingenieros, *Historia de la ingeneria Argentina*, Buenos Aires: CAI, 1981.
Colegio de Ingenieos de Venezuela, *Historia de la ingeneria en Venezuela 1861–1901 par E Arcila Farias*, Caracas: Colegio, 1961.
Fawcett, B., *Railways of the Andes*, London: Allen and Unwin, 1963.
Greve, E., *Historia de la ingenerio en Chile*, 2 volumes, Santiago: 1939.
Haine, E. A., *Railways across the Andes*, Boulder, Colorado: Privett, 1981.
Harrison, H. L., 'The railroads of Colombia, South America', *Railroad history*, volume 116, 1967, pp. 24–49.
Howarth, D., *The golden Isthmus*, London: Collins, 1966.
James, J.G., *Overseas railways and the spread of iron bridges c. 1850–1870*, Strawberry Hill: J.G. James, 1987.
McCullough, D., *The path between the seas: the creation of the Panama Canal 1870–1914*, New York: Simon and Schuster, 1977.
Railway Gazette, 'Special South American railway numbers', 22 November, 6 December, 1926.
Small, C. S., *Rails to the diggings: construction railroads of the Panama Canal*, Greenwich, Connecticut: Railroad Monographs, 1981.
Stewart, W., *Henry Meiggs: Yankee Pizarro*, Durham, NC: Duke University Press, 1946.

CONTEMPORARY SOURCES

Serials

American railroad journal, volumes 1–60, 1832–86.
Engineer, volume 1, 1856–.
Engineering, volume 1, 1866–.
Engineering and mining record, volume 1, 1866–1922.
Engineering news, volume 1, 1874–.
Engineering record, volume 1, 1877–.
Genie civil, volume 1, 1880–1973.
Ingenieria (Argentina), 1897–.
Institution of Civil Engineers, *Minutes of Proceedings*, 1837–1935.
Instituto de Ingenieros de Chile, *Anales*.
Railroad gazette, volume 1, 1873–1908.
Railway journal, (Herapeth's), 1832–93.
Railway times, volume 1, 1838–1914.
Rio de Janeiro, Club de Engenharia (previously Instituto Politicko Brazileiro Revista, vols. 1–18, 1868–88.) *Revista*, volume 1, 1887–.
Sociedad Colombiana de Ingenieros, *Anales*, 1887–.
Sociedad Cientifica de Argentina, *Anales*, 1877–.

Books

Bunau-Varilla, P., *Panama: the creation, destruction and resurrection*, London: Constable, 1913.
Castro, J. J., *Treatise on the South American railways and the great international lines*, Montevideo: Ministerio de Formento, 1893.

Clark, E., *Visit to South America*, London: Dean and Sons, 1878.
Costa y Laurent, F., *Resena historica de los Ferrocariles del Peru*, Lima: Ministerio de Formento, 1908.
Da Silva Telles, P. C., *A history of Brazilian railways*, part 1, Bromley: P. E. Waters, 1987, translation of: *As Estradas de ferro di Brasilean*, 1879, Rio de Janeiro: Brasil Railways, 1880.
Hawkshaw, J., *Reminiscences of South America*, London, 1838.
Inspectorate of Railways, *Brazilian railways: their history*, Rio de Janeiro: Neuzinger, 1893.
Lloyd, W., *A railway pioneer: notes by a civil engineer*, London: privately printed, 1900.
Pessoa, C. D. F., *Estudo descriptivo das estradas de ferro do Brasil*, Rio de Janeiro, 1886.
Pinkas, J., *Relatoria de Estrada de Ferro do Maderia a Mamore*, Rio de Janeiro: Government Press, 1885.
Trevithick, F., *Life of Richard Trevithick: with an account of his inventions*, 2 volumes, London: Spon, 1872.

CHAPTER FOURTEEN

Beatty, C., *Ferdinand de Lesseps*, London: Eyre and Spottiswoode, 1956.
Bender, C., *Who saved Natal?*, Durban: C. Bender, 1988.
Brant, E.D., *Railways of North Africa*, Newton Abbot: David and Charles, 1971.
Day, J.R., *Railways of Northern Africa*, London: Barker, 1964.
Day, J.R., *Railways of Southern Africa*, London: Barker, 1963.
Hadfield, C., *World canals: inland navigation, past and present*, Newton Abbot: David and Charles, 1986.
James, J.G., *Overseas railways and the spread of iron bridges c. 1850–1870*, Strawberry Hill: J.G. James, 1987.
Marlowe, J., *The making of the Suez Canal*, London: Cresset, 1964.
Pudney, J., *Suez: de Lessep's canal*, London: Dent, 1968.
Railway Gazette, Special African numbers, 2 volumes, London: 1927.
Varian, H.F., *Some African milestones*, Oxford: Ronald, 1953.
Weithal, L.C., ed., *The story of the Cape to Cairo Railway*, 3 volumes, London, 1923.
Wiener, L., *Les chemins de fer coloniaux de l'Afrique*, Brussels: Goemaere, 1930.
Wiener, L., *Egypte et ses chemins de fer*, Brussels, Goemaere, 1932.

CONTEMPORARY SOURCES

Serials

Annales des ponts et chaussées, volume 1, 1831–.
Civil engineer and architects journal, volumes 1–31, 1837–68.
Engineer, volume 1, 1856–.
Engineering, volume 1, 1866.
Genie Civil 1880–1973.
Institution of Civil Engineers, *Minutes of Proceedings*, volume 1, 1837–1935.
Railway journal, Herapeth's, volume 1, 1832–1893.
Railway times, volume 1, 1838–1914.

Books

Burge, C.O., *The adventures of a civil engineer*, London: Alston Rivers, 1909.
Bellefonds, L. de, *Mémoires sur les principaux travaux d'utilite publique executes en Egypte*, 2 volumes, Paris: Bertrand, 1872.
Commissioners of Inquiry upon the trade of the Cape of Good Hope, *Report*, London: HMSO, 1829.
Charles-Roux, J., *L'Isthme et le canal de Suez*, 2 volumes, Paris: Hachettes, 1901.
Lesseps, F. de, *The history of the Suez canal*, Edinburgh: Blackwood, 1876.
Lesseps, F. de, *Recollections of 40 years*, London: Chapman and Hall, 1887.
Park, M., *Travels in the interior districts of Africa*, London: 1799.
Pauling, G., *The chronicles of a contractor*, London: Constable, 1926, reprinted Bulawayo, 1969.
Voisin Bey, F.-P., *Le canal de Suez*, 7 volumes, Paris: Dunod, 1902.

INDEX

Figures in italics refer to illustrations